Helmut Debelius, Hiroyuki Tanaka & Rudie H Kuiter: Angelfishes, A Comprehensive Guide to Pomacanthidae

First English language edition 2003

Published by TMC Publishing, Chorleywood, UK

Design, editing and taxonomic decisions: Rudie H. Kuiter.
Principal authors of genera:

APOLEMICHTHYS - H. DEBELIUS
CENTROPYGE - H. TANAKA & R. KUITER
CHAETODONTOPLUS - H. TANAKA & R. KUITER
GENICANTHUS - H. TANAKA
HOLACANTHUS - H. DEBELIUS
PARACENTROPYGE - H. TANAKA
POMACANTHUS - H. DEBELIUS
PYGOPLITES - H. TANAKA

Print and production: Grupo M & G Difusión S.L

TMC Publishing
Solesbridge Lane,
Chorleywood, Herts WD3 5SX
United Kingdom

Tel: +44 (0) 1923 284151 Fax: +44 (0) 1923 285840
Email: info@tmc-publishing.com
Website: www.tmc-publishing.com

ISBN 0-9539097-5-1

The Marine Fish Families Series

Angelfishes

A Comprehensive Guide to Pomacanthidae

Helmut Debelius

Hiroyuki Tanaka

Rudie H Kuiter

TMC
publishing

TMC Publishing, Chorleywood, UK

ACKNOWLEDGEMENTS: our thanks to the many contributors of photographs and information. Jerry Allen, Yukio Aramata, Philippe Bacchet, Neville Coleman, Steve Drogin, Graham Edgar, Carlos Ferreira, Sergio Floeter, Malcolm Francis, Lola Fritzsche, João Gasparini, Bob Halstead, Tomonori Hirata, John Hoover, Kazunori (GARUDA) Igarashi, Tsuyoshi Kawamoto, Dennis King, Randall Kosaki, Hiroshi Kobayashi, Yves Lefevre, Osmar Luis-Júnior, Hajime Masuda, Scott Michael, Tomoyo Mizutani, Atsushi Morioka, Osamu Morishita, Yasuhiro Morita, Robert Myers, Hiroshi Nagano, Tsuneo Nakamura, Yutaka Niino, Richard Pyle, Ross Robertson, Ed Robinson, Frank Schneidewind, Hiroshi Senou, Akihiko Shinchi, Marcel Staebler, Roger Steene, Mark Strickland, Takamasa Tonozuka, Hiroshi Takeuchi, Hiroyuki Tatsuuma, Greg De Valle, Hugues Vitry, Fenton Walsh, Jim Watt, Keith Wilson, Phil Woodhead, Satoshi (Marshall) Yoshii who generously supplied many superb photographs. We would also like to thank all those photographers who provided information with their photographs.

A special thanks to Steve Drogin who hosted 2 expeditional live-aboard trips into the South Pacific recently, in which Helmut Debelius participated. Frank Baensch for providing the information on cultivation and larval development of several *Centropyge* spp, and Osmar Luis-Júnior for writing about the *Holacanthus* colour morphs of St. Pauls Rocks.

Photo-credits: all photographers are fully credited in the captions.

TABLE OF CONTENTS

Introduction..3
  Angelfishes 4
  Discovering a new Angelfish..6
  Collecting Angelfishes..8
  Spawning and development
    The Culture and Larval Development of three Pygmy Angelfish 10
  Colour Morphs & Hybrids 14
About this book 16

SYSTEMATIC SECTION
Family POMACANTHIDAE - GENERA CONTENTS...17
  Genus *POMACANTHUS*..18
  Genus *POMACANTHUS* - SUBGENERA PICTURE INDEX...19
    Euxiphipops 19
    Pomacanthoides...29
    Pomacanthus..52
  Genus *HOLACANTHUS* 60
  Genus *Holacanthus* - SUBGENERA PICTURE INDEX 60
    Holacanthus...61
    Angelichthys..64
    Plitops...76
  Genus *APOLEMICHTHYS* 84
  Genus *CHAETODONTOPLUS* 100
  Genus *PYGOPLITES*...134
  Genus *GENICANTHUS*..138
  Genus *PARACENTROPYGE* 160
  Genus *CENTROPYGE* 168

Bibliography 206
Index 206

INTRODUCTION

The members of the family Pomacanthidae are generally known as angelfishes and, like their nearest cousins, the butterflyfishes, are regarded by many divers and aquarists as being amongst the most beautiful and majestic fishes in the sea. Some 88 species are here recognised, divided into 8 genera with members variously distributed in all tropical seas. The largest genus *Centropyge* comprises 32 species under the present classification, but there are some distinct groups within and some have been placed in subgenera. As this genus is under study by Richard Pyle (Bishop Museum), we have not attempted to group them into subgenera. The next largest genus with 14 species is *Chaetodontoplus* and the generic status of some is in doubt and, as unpublished preliminary research has suggested, is in need of revision. The majority of species occur on shallow reefs in coral, algae and sponge zones, most going little deeper than about 30 m, but where conditions are pristine and water is very clear, many species go much deeper and few species only live deep (over 100 m).

The family Pomacanthidae is part of the large order of Perciformes that includes many of the fishes encountered on coral reefs, such as the damselfishes, wrasses, and the butterflyfishes. Angelfishes feature a large and distinctive backward-protruding spine from the lower corner of the gill-plate (cheek-spine) from which the family name was derived. This cheek-spine is diagnostic for all the species, even at juvenile stage, and readily separates any angelfishes from butterflyfishes that may be similar in shape. Most angelfishes are robust with compressed, ovate to rhomboid shaped bodies, covered with small or tiny scales, and have a continous dorsal fin. The mouth is small and jaws are set with many small, usually tricuspid teeth that are used for grazing algae or scraping sponges and other sessile invertebrates. Few species combine their diet with a variety of foods and some are planktivores. Diversity is expressed in diagnostic colour patterns that are often dramatically different within a genus and to a lesser extent between closely related species or siblings.

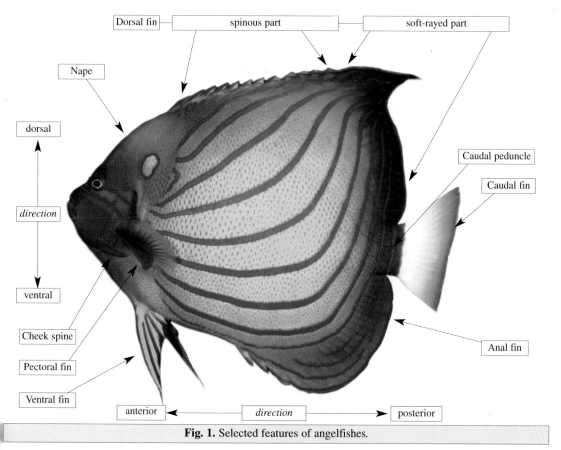

Fig. 1. Selected features of angelfishes.

ANGELFISHES

Members of the family Pomacanthidae are generally known as angelfishes and few have names that do not incorporate it in their specific name. These have names such as Lemon Peel, Coral Beauty, Jumping Bean, etc that are a reflection of certain features, either brilliant colour or certain behaviour, or maybe a localised name. The species in the genus *Centropyge* are generally known as pygmy angelfishes, of course because of their small size. Many species feature amazing colours and patterns that may seem to have been created by an abstract artist. Some of the large species, with their combined beautiful colours and graceful movements, have a truly majestic appearance, giving rise to names such as Regal-, Majestic-, Emperor-, Queen- or King Angelfish. The sheer beauty of these fishes mean they are favourites amongst the diver fish-watchers, and are also sought after as pets for the aquarium fish trade. Species that live in remote regions fetch high prices, and are amongst the most expensive marine fishes sold in pet shops. Unfortunately, angelfishes do not occur in large numbers on reefs, they are often territorial and may be long lived. Local collecting of such species can have a severe negative impact on populations and needs to be done with common sense, especially in the case of species with a small geographical distribution. Ideally, large adults are left alone and only juveniles or subadults are collected. The decline of some populations of angelfishes has led to temporary import bans on all species of Pomacanthidae in some countries, but now a number of species are aquacultured successfully for the aquarium trade. Large species, such as those in *Pomacanthus,* are spawned from taking gametes artificially from gravid females and sexually active males, whilst pygmy species are left to produce these naturally (see page 10). Fishes produced this way are a much better option for the aquarist as they are used to captivity and readily accept all kinds of food, and pressure on the wild populations is reduced. In some areas (eg Lord Howe Island, Australia) collecting is not permitted and if species are offered for sale, endemic to such areas, they may have been collected illegally.

HD's aquarium in 1983, the home for three angelfish species. A *Chaetodontoplus, Centropyge* and *Pomacanthus.* Keeping members of different genera is a good idea as most species tend to be aggressive to their own kind or close relatives when kept in a small space together. Note the background, providing lots of small hiding places and passages to swim through. On the wall above the aquarium, a selection of angelfish illustrations that were originally created for the famous fish Atlas by Peter Bleeker, the Dutch army doctor who named many of the earlier described angelfishes from the Indo-Pacific region.

All angelfishes are associated with reefs. They use crevices and often favour slopes with large boulders where they can swim through passages to avoid or escape predators, as well as dense coral areas, or they swim below large coral plates. Shipwrecks are also popular with the large angelfish species. Coral-rich habitats or shipwrecks are often the home for many different species. A perfect example is the 'Liberty', one of the most frequented dive-sites in Bali, from which many pictures in this book came. Here you can see numerous pairs of *Pomacanthus imperator* (Indian and Pacific forms), *P. xanthometopon, P. annularis,* several *Centropyge* spp, *Apolemichthys,* and *Pygoplites.* In such places the fish are used to divers and can easily be approached at close range, an ideal photo-shoot locality for all kinds. Small postlarval stages are extremely secretive and are often not seen until several weeks old, often hiding and restricting themselves to narrow crevices or small caves. Over time they become more confident and start venturing out, but stay close to the bottom, always ready to escape into some small hole. The small species often remain secretive but may form a small aggregation to enable them to move around more, especially on shallow reefs where algae may form an important part of their diet. The large species are often seen solitary or in pairs, but a few may school to feed on plankton, to spawn or migrate. Although they swim about openly on reefs, they are very familiar with their surroundings and know every hole or passage in their territory, and most large species have an extensive home range. Many juvenile as well as adult angelfishes will engage in cleaning other, often much larger fishes, such as sunfish, as well as checking out turtles, mantas, sharks, etc, to remove certain parasites or algae.

Above: HD, and the eye-catching giant mural of *Pomacanthus annularis,* his favourite fish, on the side of his 3-story house in Germany.

It was a case of love at first sight when Helmut Debelius caught his first angelfish in the wild, a subadult *Pomacanthus annularis* in Ceylonese waters assisting the well known fish exporter Rodney Jonklaas in collecting ornamental fish. This was a surprise for Rodney as *P. annularis* is rarely found in this area. This fish became the logo of his letterhead and business cards, but it didn't stop there. One would get a big surprise when turning the corner into his street and seeing the giant mural on his house (above). Years later it almost broke his heart when he discovered a blue-ringed angel grilled on a fire place in a fishermen's village at Halmahera, Indonesia (below). However, they are reputed to be good to eat!

Hiroyuki Tanaka, keeps some of the smaller species in his home aquarium in Japan and whilst many are purchased, some juveniles can be caught locally in his area, some expatriating from the more tropical waters that drift in as larval stages with the summer currents. A similar situation exists on the east coast of Australia where Rudie Kuiter -living in Sydney then- collected a number of postlarval stages of angelfishes that are illustrated in this book. Small individuals that were collected from the wild would grow very fast. Often doubling their size in a matter of weeks, but gradually slowing down in growth-rate, which also happens in the wild. Those species that settled in the Sydney region are mainly algae feeders and to a lesser extent sponge feeders, certainly not exclusive sponge feeders which contributed to their success in captivity. The most common expatriate there is *Centropyge tibicen,* and usually a few *Pomacanthus semicirculatus* would be found by some keen collectors every summer. Interestingly these were usually picked up by beginners on snorkel at 1 or 2 m depth.

DISCOVERING A NEW ANGELFISH

During my 1988 visit to Flic en Flac, off the west coast of Mauritius, I made the acquaintance of Daniel Pelicier, a remarkable fisherman who supplies the local fish market, exports tropical ornamental fish, and trades in stonefish venom. Seeing Daniel catch a stone fish with his bare hands was quite an experience. With remarkable agility he would grab the venomous creature by the mouth and keep its thrashing body at bay. Institutes from all over the world acquire stonefish venom from him, in order to produce an antidote. After extracting the venom, Daniel would fry up some of finest fish fillets I'd ever tasted!

Daniel was hired by a South African shark investigator extremely eager to examine a Mauritius shark. I was delegated the task of securing the fresh bait at a depth of 50 m when something caught my eye. Focusing my 100 mm macro lens, I hardly dared to breathe. A pygmy angelfish with its typical gill-cover spines is a familiar sight to me, but I'd never seen one with such a deep-blue hue before. It was quite dark down there and difficult to get a good shot of this lively algae-feeder. I activated the shutter the very moment the little fellow looked directly into the camera. The bright flash scared him off. I waited for a few seconds, hoping that he would show himself again, but being at 52 m my dive-computer reminded me emphatically that time had run out. The photograph may not have been first-rate, but good enough for angelfish experts to eventually confirm my suspicion that I had found a new *Centropyge*.

Richard Pyle, an ichthyologist from Hawaii working on his dissertation on pygmy angelfish at the time, couldn't wait to accompany me on my next trip to Mauritius. It was 1990, in March, the prime time to dive unless a cyclone should approach. Rich said "Helmut, this angelfish is not as scarce as you think it is. You simply didn't dive deep enough, and at 60 to 70 m we are bound to come across groups of them." Rich had gained a lot of experience with deep-dwelling Pacific pygmy angelfish and so I believed him. However, with all due respect to his enthusiasm, I prefer to avoid such depths, but we were both optimistic about finding and capturing the needed specimens somewhere along the steep drop-off as none other than Daniel was taking us directly to Rempart l'herbe, the site.

The weather was perfect, but quite unexpectedly Daniel refused to dive with us on this particular reef. He considered this to be "his" private hunting grounds and didn't want others catching fish there. Somewhat annoyed we left Flic en Flac and it became clear to us that we would have to search for another site. The eastern shores of Mauritius are much

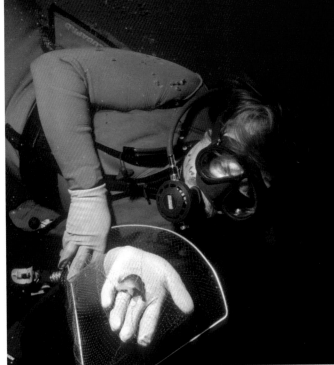
The first specimen captured.

too shallow, and where along the western coast could we come across another reef lying deeper than 50 m? Ichthyologists had dived for decades all over the western shores of Mauritius, but no-one had seen our blue Pygmy angel fish. Luckily Hugues Vitry, a dive operator based near Trou aux Biches, knew the local diving sites like the back of his hand and he gave us new hope. Radio warnings of an approaching cyclone did not help our impatience, but at long last, Hugues was able to take us on a special dive. A wall he was familiar with, starting at 45 m and dropping off steeply to unknown depths. Hugues and I dove along the wall at 50 m while Rich vanished into the deep. Just three minutes down and I detected my first specimen. Like a typical Pygmy angel fish, this 6 cm or so long fish was darting in and out of crevices along the wall picking at algae. I held my breath as I moved in closer with my camera. Taking shots when I could, did I get this vivacious little creature on film? It would disappear into the dark cracks along the wall for minutes at the time, seeming like an eternity, but fortunately kept showing itself again and again. When Hugues finally tapped

My reward, *Centropyge debelius*, with fins spread and showing good colour, and *Canthigaster smithi*, a curious onlooker.

me on the shoulder I glanced at my computer, it indicated 13 minutes at 52 m. It was high time for us to ascend. No sign of Richard anywhere. Whilst anxiously hanging onto the decompression line, I anticipated his catch from the deep and hoped and prayed that at least one of the photographs I took would turn out well. When Rich finally emerged he had a few *Chaetodon mitratus* in his box along with two *Centropyge acanthops*, but no blue pygmy angel fish. Even at depths of 75 m he didn't find the fish we were looking for!

The next day Hugues was fully occupied with customers that he did not want to take down that deep. In the meantime the cyclone had moved in closer with dark clouds over Mauritius and waves along the eastern coast several metres high, but the waters along the western coast were still perfectly smooth. Time was running out on us and the next morning we headed out to sea with a rising wind. Weather conditions were getting worse and Hugues could hardly make out his reference points on land. As we descended to look for the site where I had previously found the blue pygmy angel fish it was already getting dark at a depth of 15 m. Hugues had anchored in a different position so it was difficult to locate. At 50 m I began checking the wall with my torch on and in less than 5 minutes I found "my" angel fish. My shout of joy must have been pretty loud as in seconds Rich was right next to me. He grinned and in a split second had the fish trapped in his net. In all the excitement to take photos of this event I had nearly used up my supply of air.

Forewarned by experience - a cyclone had smashed his previous wooden craft against the shore - we helped Hugues to haul his boat inland as far as possible. Diving during the following few days would have been out of the question. However, that didn't bother me very much, as I spent the time admiring the blue pygmy angel fish swimming happily in the aquarium that we had set up for it. Rich took the specimen back with him to Hawaii, even managing to keep it alive. This scientist could now proceed with its classification, especially after I sent him my photographs which turned out to be very useful. The blue pygmy angel fish has since been scientifically described and was named after me as *Centropyge debelius*.

Left: a stamp of approval by the Mauritius Postal service, featuring *Centropyge debelius*.

Right: the discovery of this species in the Aldabra Atoll in 1997 by Stefan Okonek, a videographer, was a big surprise. This find, at the most western islands of the Seychelles, near Africa, represented a great extension of its geographical range, and it was filmed at a depth of only 20 m.

COLLECTING ANGELFISHES

In the Maldives (central Indian Ocean) collectors only use small and large hand-nets to catch ornamental fishes, which are transferred to plastic bags whilst on the seabed. Some of the larger Angelfishes, such as *Pomacanthus imperator* or *Apolemichthys trimaculatus* are usually collected at depths between 20 to 25 m and are slowly taken to the surface. On the shore, large angelfishes are kept by themselves in holding facilities as they are likely to fight and could do a lot of damage to each other with their cheek spines. This also makes it easy to have specimens ready for packing and shipping. Being situated on a coral atoll has the advantage of the readily available high quality water to accommodate the fish. However such a place would be perfect for aquaculture, a much preferred method for marketing marine fishes, especially such species as the larger angelfishes which are territorial and never present in large numbers on these reefs. Local populations could easily suffer from over-collecting.

Author HD joined professional collectors in the Caribbean, Sea of Cortez, Hawaii, Southeast Asia, in the central and western Indian Ocean, and in the Red Sea over the years to see how ornamental fishes, especially angelfishes, are collected. In the early 1980s he produced a 45 minute TV-documentary to highlight the negative impact of the usual practices of using cyanide by fish-collectors in the Philippines.

The Philippines and Sri Lanka were the first to export marine ornamental fishes for the international market in the late 1950s. Extensive collecting reduced the population numbers, especially those of angelfishes. This resulted in the fishermen starting to use new and more efficient methods in the 1970s. The use of cyanide was widespread, which knocked fish unconscious and made them easy to collect, including species that hide and are normally difficult to catch, such as the pygmy angelfishes. The fishes were then revived in clear water, swimming around and looking fine, but would be short lived. After arriving in pet shops and then being sold, for no apparent reason they would be found dead. Postmortems soon revealed that these fishes suffered from liver damage and survived only for a short time in the aquarist's tank. The embarrassed ornamental fish trade in the USA reacted swiftly and threatened a complete fish import ban on fish from the Philippines. Also US-organisations like the "International Marine Alliance" settled in Manila to stop the ornamental fish collecters using cyanide.

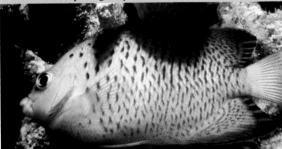
Affected by cyanide, this pygmy angelfish laying on the bottom is easily caught by hand.

An expert, sent by an American ornamental-fish wholesaler to the Philippines, educating his collectors.

Collecting *Pomacanthus chrysurus*

In Kenya, western Indian Ocean, the local collectors catch ornamental fish on the shallow reefs of the Shimoni-area, simply by snorkelling. Surprisingly, they were catching juveniles as well as adult *Pomacanthus chrysurus*, but in a place that seemed rather an unlikely habitat at first. The reefs were covered extensively with tall soft corals that looked like algae from a distance. The fish had plenty of places to hide, but the collectors brought up quite a few. As these specimens were brought up from such shallow depths, these angelfishes did not suffer any buoyancy problems on the surface.

Right: a subadult *Pomacanthus chrysurus* is carefully removed from the monofilament handnet and will be taken up to the holding bucket floating on the surface in an inner-tube of a tire. Such a bucket has numerous small holes so the water stays fresh

The Culture and Larval Development of three Pygmy Angelfish species:
Centropyge fisheri, Centropyge loriculus and *Centropyge flavissima*

By Frank Baensch*

Over the past decade, I've had the opportunity to study a number of *Centropyge* species, both in the wild and in the aquarium. My research has focused on their reproductive biology and captive propagation. Recently, I was successful at raising the larvae through metamorphosis of 3 species: *C. fisheri, C. flavissima* and *C. loriculus*. The former two species had never been raised in captivity. The work was done at my garage-based hatchery facility, Reef Culture Technologies LLC (RCT), located on Oahu, Hawaii.

The *Centropyge* species that I've studied are pelagic spawners, releasing their eggs directly into the water column. Every evening during the twilight hours, males undergo an intense mating ritual with each mature female in its harem. Spawning is commenced when the male rises with a female about a metre above the reef substrate, while "nuzzling" her abdominal area. Climax is marked by a forceful thrust of his snout against the abdomen followed by split second body reversal, which lines up the orifices of both sexes. Eggs and sperm are then released in a single burst and fertilisation occurs. The presence of an oil globule causes the eggs to rise from the spawning site, just above the reef substrate, to the plankton rich surface waters. *Centropyge* species that adapt well to captivity will often spawn without any special provisions. In fact, aquarium spawning is frequently witnessed by hobbyists and has been reported for about 15 species. However, egg production can be poor and random when the proper diet and environmental conditions are lacking. In my experience, the keys to consistently achieving large, fertile spawns have been:

1. Starting out with healthy, mature fish. Proper selection and quarantine is important here.
2. Conditioning them on 2–3 daily feedings of a diverse seafood diet, including fish roe, spirulina and astaxanthin.
3. Providing them with 14–16 hours of light and water temperatures between 26–28°C.
4. Keeping them in no less than a 300 litre tank with a minimal height of 50 cm to allow for sufficient rise during spawning.
5. Maintaining adequate water quality.

I have now spawned 10 fish species at my facility, continuously over several years. These include *Centropyge multicolor, C. shepardi, C. potteri, C. bispinosa*, plus the 3 *Centropyge* species I have raised. Each spawning group is kept in a 300–600 litre tank and consists of one large male and one to two smaller females of different sizes. The females produce between 300 and 2000 fertile eggs every night. Collecting pelagic eggs is simple since they are buoyant. My brood-stock tanks have surface outflows that spill into a collecting tank. Here the eggs are concentrated in a screened container. In the morning the eggs are washed into a 1-litre beaker with fresh saltwater. Pelagic eggs that die during development will sink to the bottom as will any unwanted material, such algae or leftover foods. Healthy, fertile eggs remain buoyant and accumulate at the rim. These can then be carefully transferred with a pipette into the larval rearing tank before they hatch.

Centropyge larvae are very primitive at hatching. Egg development is short and newly hatched larvae lack eyes, a mouth, a digestive tract and functional fins. As the yolk gets depleted these develop. At 3–4 days after hatching the larvae are able to start feeding. Providing the correct diet and environment then becomes critical to further development. Of particular importance here is the size, quality and number of food organisms available to the larvae. *C. fisheri, C. flavissima* and *C. loriculus* have a very similar ontogeny up to metamorphosis. Interestingly, the near transparent larvae undergo noticeable vascularisation during the first 2 weeks of development. This "reddening" only occurs if they are growing and healthy and is an excellent indicator of how well they are cared for. After 10 days significant size variation within each larval cohort becomes apparent. As the larvae grow they become increasingly laterally compressed and take on a silver colouration, two traits that provide camouflage in the dangerous pelagic environment. Pigmentation develops on the dorsal area. Each species starts metamorphosis at a different time. Once this transition has begun the larvae gradually develop the colouration of a juvenile over several weeks. They behave less erratically and become more stationary, orienting themselves closer to dark surfaces such as the tank sides. At this time they can be transferred to a grow-out tank.

My first rearing success occurred back in November of 2001 with *Centropyge fisheri*. To the best of my knowledge this is the first pygmy angelfish species to be raised in captivity. *C. fisheri* is a Hawaiian endemic species that …

***Frank Baensch** is a marine biologist and avid fish culturist and has been keeping saltwater aquarium species for over 25 years. He specialises in the propagation of marine ornamentals and has developed rearing techniques for difficult to rear marine aquarium fishes and shrimps. All photographs by the author.

D = 0.7 mm D = 0.7 mm D = 0.75 mm

Fig. 1. Embryo of (left to right) *Centropyge fisheri, C. flavissima & C. loriculus,* at 12 hours post fertilization.

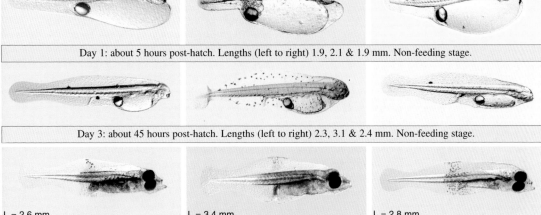

Day 1: about 5 hours post-hatch. Lengths (left to right) 1.9, 2.1 & 1.9 mm. Non-feeding stage.

Day 3: about 45 hours post-hatch. Lengths (left to right) 2.3, 3.1 & 2.4 mm. Non-feeding stage.

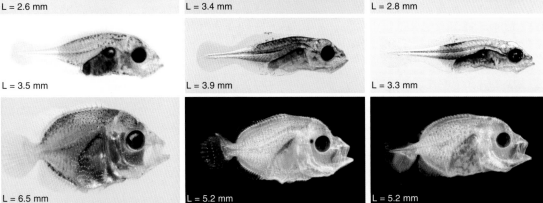

L = 2.6 mm L = 3.4 mm L = 2.8 mm

L = 3.5 mm L = 3.9 mm L = 3.3 mm

L = 6.5 mm L = 5.2 mm L = 5.2 mm

Fig. 2. Larval development of (left column to right column) *Centropyge fisheri, C. flavissima & C. loriculus*. From Day 1–3 (non-feeding stages), and from Day 5 (after first feeding) to 21–25 days development. L. is total length

Day 50 L = 13 mm Day 52 L = 22 mm Day 90 L = 24 mm

Fig. 3. Post-larval stages of (left column to right column) *Centropyge fisheri, C. flavissima & C. loriculus*. Gradually becoming more colourful and beginning to show markings recognisable as the species. L. is total length.

is rarely seen in the aquarium trade. One of the benefits of this species, aside from its hardiness, is that it is relatively small and will produce quality spawns in tanks as small as 100 litres. Each of my females produces between 500–900 eggs a night. The eggs of *C. fisheri* measure about 0.7 mm in diameter and hatch after 16 hours post fertilisation at 27°C. The larvae start feeding on the morning of the fourth day, averaging about 2.5 mm in length. At 26–28°C, their length doubles approximately every 3 weeks. The larvae start metamorphosis near day 45, at a length of 10 mm or more. As they settle, the dorsal and anal fins darken, the ventral fins show a hint of dark blue colour and the body becomes covered with small brown spots. These areas gradually fill in over the next 15 days. They complete their transition near day 60 when they resemble miniature adults. At this stage I transferred them out of the larval rearing tank.

In January of 2002, I applied the basic technique developed with *Centropyge fisheri* to *C. flavissima* and *C. loriculus*. Both species originated from the Marshall Islands and have been spawning at my facility for more than three years in 250 litre aquariums. My *C. flavissima* females each produce between 200 and 600 eggs every night. Fecundity is much higher in my *C. loriculus* pairs; averaging over 1000 eggs a night! Fertility is usually above 90%.

The eggs of *C. loriculus* resemble those of *C. fisheri,* both in size and pigmentation. At 27°C, both larval species start hatching near noon of their first day and begin feeding sometime during the fourth day. Vascularisation begins on day 5 and silver body colouration develops around day 20. Morphology, growth and pigmentation are similar for about the first 30 days. After this time *C. loriculus* larvae begin to develop a reddish hue on the dorsal area and can be easily identified. The larvae grow and become increasingly laterally compressed over the next 20 days but change little in colouration. Near day 45

they develop dark pigmentation on their dorsal and anal fins and their body gradually takes on a more reddish tint. The larvae truly start to settle around day 80, developing more juvenile like behaviour and strong red pigmentation. At this time they can be transferred and converted to artificial diets.

The eggs of *Centropyge flavissima* average 0.75 mm and have a yellow oil globule. The oil globule is visible through to day 4. This makes it easy to distinguish *C. flavissima* larvae from the other two species during that stage. Species that produce large eggs usually have proportionally large larvae throughout development. This holds true for the *Centropyge* as well. The larvae of *C. flavissima* hatch out larger and grow faster than those of *C. fisheri* and *C. loriculus*. First feeding begins during the third day after hatching and vascularisation is first noticeable near the end of the fourth day. Three weeks after hatching the larvae begin to laterally compress and develop yellow pigmentation on the dorsal area. Metamorphosis starts near day 45, much like *C. fisheri,* but at over 20 mm in length. At this time the post larvae develop an obvious black spot on the body centre. Over the next 2 weeks the body becomes increasingly yellow and blue colouration surrounds the black spot, the eye and the edge of the anterior fins. I was able to safely transfer the first juveniles to grow-out after 53 days in the larval rearing tank. By day 70 all fish had developed full colouration. Thirty days later the black spot almost completely disappears, at which time the juveniles begin to resemble an adult fish. Now, as many as 41 *Centropyge fisheri* juveniles are 231 days old, 8 *C. loriculus* 87 days old, and 7 *C. flavissima* 85 days old. The fish are all healthy and feeding on gel diet. Survival was lower for the latter two species because I invested considerably less time rearing them. A few months ago I set up a *Centropyge fisheri* harem with twelve of my tank-raised juveniles. Last week I collected my first batch of fertile eggs from this F1 generation! The F2 larvae are now 8

Postlarval and juvenile *Centropyge flavissima*, now easily recognised and beautifully coloured at about 80 days old.

days old and actively feeding. I'm eager to see if survival and growth can be improved upon.

In mid-January of 2002 two other research groups had breakthroughs culturing marine angelfishes here in Hawaii. Karen Britain at the Waikiki Aquarium was successful in raising the highly valued Hawaiian endemic *Genicanthus personatus*. At the same time Oceanic Institute announced their breakthrough with their *Centropyge loriculus*. All of us achieved these results without collaborating! I know this may be hard to believe, considering this group of reef fishes has been worked on for over 25 years.

Centropyge fisheri, successfully raised juvenile.

So how was it done? As for myself, the basic technique was developed with *Centropyge fisheri* through excessive care, patience and intense observation of the larvae. The rearing days were long, near 18 hours, and involved much trial and error. I would learn, revise my method and try again. For me, closing the *Centropyge* life-cycle was not a single breakthrough, involving some special food organism or environmental condition, but rather a number of small advances or learning experiences that, when put together correctly, allowed the larvae to survive. Of course, a little luck was involved as well. There are a few specifics I can reveal at this time:

Centropyge loriculus, successfully raised juvenile.

1. The dietary and environmental requirements of the three larval species are similar.
2. Larval food up to metamorphosis consisted mostly of wild plankton.
3. Newly hatched and enriched brine shrimp were primarily used to bring the larvae through metamorphosis.
4. Once settled the juveniles could quickly be converted to my homemade gel diet.

I plan to make this technique more available to other culturists once I have developed it and explored its potential application to other difficult-to-rear pelagic spawners.

Centropyge multicolor, the next species to be cultivated and a successfully raised juvenile.

A beautiful sight, *Centropyge* spp postlarvae transforming into juveniles.

COLOUR MORPHS & HYBRIDS

The colouration of males and females is virtually the same for most angelfishes. Only those in the genus *Genicanthus* show marked sexual dimorphism. Juveniles of the larger angelfishes often have their own unique colouration with no resemblance to their parents. Within species, colouration is very similar between individuals of comparable sizes, sometimes there are small aberrations in patterns of stripes or spots, but on the other hand some strange colour morphs appear in certain areas. E.g., at St. Pauls Rocks, a small island at some distance off the Brazilian coast, a very isolated place, its population of *Holacanthus ciliaris*

produces a number of strange colour morphs (see p. 72), thought to be caused by in-breeding. However, this needs investigation as some captured morphs changed to the normal colours after some weeks in captivity. Some of the pygmy angelfishes have colour morphs that appear to be seasonal and may be related to sexual behaviour. This seems to be the case with *Centropyge bispinosa* in the Coral Sea, east of the Great Barrier Reef (see picture on left). Such individuals were captured and changed back to their normal colouration after some weeks (see p. 177).

Unusual colour morphs are produced when species cross-breed, usually close relatives that occur sympatric, or overlap in their geographical range. Normally hybrids are sterile and have no further influence on the species. Colouration varies greatly between individuals from the same parent species. Features of both parents, colour patterns or fin-shapes is evident in an unbalanced mix. Parent species may be obvious on colour patterns and usually one would be obvious, but sometimes the second one is difficult to determine. The hybrid individual in the picture below is most similar in colour to *Centropyge flavissima*, clearly one parent, whilst the other parent is not obvious at all, but is likely to be *C. vrolikii*, a sympatric species that often hybridises with the former.

Centropyge bispinosa. Morph from Coral Sea. Fenton Walsh.

Centropyge flavissima X *vrolikii*(?). from Vanuatu. Length 5 cm. Fenton Walsh.

Pomacanthus navarchus X *xanthometopon*. Aquarium. Robert Myers. The parent species occur sympatric in the tropical West Pacific. Hybrids are likely to occur when one of the species is rare and cannot find a partner of its own kind.

Pomacanthus chrysurus X *maculosus*. Kenya. Helmut Debelius. In Kenya the *P. chrysurus* is the more common species, whilst *P. maculosus* is an expatriate from more northern regions and may pair up with the former, producing hybrids as below.

ABOUT THIS BOOK

This book is the 5th volume of The Marine Fish Families Series, dealing with species on a global scale. The aim is to create a series of books that comprehensively covers closely related or certain groups of fish with photographs, as a pictorial guide, primarily for the purpose of identifying species and to find out what is known about them. A volume may comprise a group, or related groups of fishes that belong in a single family, several families, or just part of a family, depending on how small or large such a group is. The first four volumes dealt with the orders of Syngnathiformes, Acanthuroidei, Labridae (in part, the 2nd part of Labridae will be produced as separate volume), and Chaetodontidae.

All the known species of the family Pomacanthidae are covered in this volume. Where possible, each species is illustrated with photographs to show different stages, geographical variations, as well as the same form of a wide-ranging species from different geographical zones. The genera and species are arranged in order of relationship or similarity. Notes on behaviour are primarily based on the author's observations in the field or in an aquarium. Aquarium details are mostly generalised in the genus or subgenus accounts, but some additional information may be provided with certain species. Notes on habitat, size and behaviour will give the reader further information with regards to keeping species in captivity. Illustrations are of living fishes and in their natural habitat whenever possible. Additional aquarium material may be used to illustrate colour changes or rarely photographed species in the wild or a picture of a freshly caught specimen as a last resort, especially when dealing with deep water species. Pictorial contents pages provide easy and quick-find facilities for the different genera or species-complexes. Photographs are captioned with their scientific name, locality, depth, size and the name of the contributing photographer (as/if provided by the photographer). The genera each have their own general introduction which gives information on gender, type-species, number of species, range and habitat, behaviour and requirements with regards to husbandry, if known.

NAMES

The species are presented with their current common and scientific name, followed by their original scientific name, and the author and date of descriptions. The scientific name of a species is binominal. The first part is the genus, that may be shared by closely related species, and the second part is the species name, that is unique. The common and scientific names are presented in a coloured box, separate above the main species text, and is immediately recognisable on the page. The text for each species begins with the original name, its author and date, when it was first described. The original genus may differ from the one in use now. A species may have been described and placed in the genus that was thought to be correct at the time, but other species that belong in the same genus may have been placed in a different genus. In such cases, the oldest name is valid and the later used name corrected. Some of the included species may have been discovered only recently and are not named scientifically. These are placed in the appropriate genus and treated as 'sp', short for species. Some species were described several times by different authors and sometimes the same author described the male and female as different species. There are approximately 180 nominal pomacanthid-names, involving about 88 valid species, plus some species that are not yet named.

Some species may be known under several common names which may reflect different forms or their use in different countries or trades. Divers may call a species one name and aquarists may use another for the same species. Scientists often translate the meaning of their scientific name, which often makes no sense and this can be very confusing for the layman. Using scientific names as actual common names is even more confusing and is not encouraged in this series of books. Usually a single name is given for a species. If there is a second well-established name, it may be included in the text. Scientific names help to make sure that we are talking internationally about the same taxon, but in some groups the taxonomy is badly in need of work and names are changing regularly on different taxon levels. In some cases a common name carries more weight than its scientific one. Compared to many other fishes, the taxonomy of the family Pomacanthidae is reasonably well-established, but on a species level. Some genera are in need of revision, and in some cases there are some problems with the assignment of certain species to a particular genus. The principal arguable points are usually on a subspecies or subgenus level, 'where to draw the line' so to speak. Often species are lumped together because scientists can not tell them apart, but divers and aquarists often find that behaviour plays an additional role in recognising different species.

Pomacanthus **18**

Pomacanthus **18**

Pomacanthus **18**

Holacanthus **60**

Holacanthus **60**

Apolemichthys **84**

Chaetodontoplus **100**

Chaetodontoplus **100**

Chaetodontoplus **100**

Pygoplites **134**

Genicanthus **138**

Genicanthus **138**

Paracentropyge **160**

Centropyge **168**

Centropyge **168**

Masculine. Type species: *Chaetodon arcuatus* Linnaeus 1758. Represented by 13 species worldwide, divided into 3 subgenera, the Atlantic *Pomacanthus* with 2 species, the mainly West Pacific *Euxiphipops* with 3 species, and the rest in the widespread Indo-Pacific subgenus *Pomacanthodes*. The Latin name *Pomacanthus* relates to the large cheek spine and thus to the anatomical and diagnostic feature of all angelfishes. Most members of the various subgenera are beautifully coloured from the moment they settle from a pelagic stage on the reef. The adults are looked upon as THE foremost 'bill-board' coloured reef dwellers. When talking about angelfishes, it will be the members of this group that are the "true" angelfishes. The various species grow from about 30 to almost 60 cm, and thus are among the largest angelfishes, leaving an immediate impression on an encountering diver. The species are uniquely coloured and easily identified by their different patterns. Males and females of the same species show almost no difference, but their juveniles have a unique and completely different pattern from the adult. An inexperienced observer would recognise these animals as a distinct species and even non-diving scientists did, describing species based on the juvenile patterns of species that were already named (*Pomacanthus nicobariensis*, *P. striatus*). Most species are inter-specifically aggressive and occupy large territories, which may be as large as several hundred square metres. The majority of species occur either singly or in pairs. Only the Caribbean *P. arcuatus* and the south African *P. rhomboides* are exceptions, hunting plankton in loose groups in the open water, even close to the surface.

Many of the large angelfishes (e.g. *Pomacanthus arcuatus* and *P. maculosus*) are often curious towards divers and may approach an observer or photographer closely. When feeling threatened, some of them (e.g. *P. semicirculatus* and *P. imperator)* produce loud audible noises (bongo-like), which usually surprise a diver at first, as humans have no sense of direction of sound underwater. Some of the 'true' angelfish species grow simply too large to keep in the usual home aquarium, although they normally do not reach their maximum length when in a restricted environment. Those purchased as juveniles may have difficulties achieving their final colouration, so this interesting process remains incomplete. Although *Pomacanthus*-species are primarily found as pairs in the wild, members of the same species usually fight amongst themselves in captivity. Unfortunately, many that are captured as adults reject food, and consequently do not survive for long. When purchasing fish, it is important to remember that juvenile angelfishes are much more adaptable than adults. If the initial problems are overcome, all species of *Pomacanthus* are hardy and long-lived. E.g. the Nancy Tropical Aquarium, a public aquarium in France, kept *Pomacanthus navarchus* for 26 years and *Pomacanthus imperator* for 15 years!

List of subgenera and species.

			(p. **19**)
	Subgenus ***Euxiphipops***		(p. **19**)
1.	*P. navarchus*	*Holacanthus navarchus* Cuvier, 1831. Java, Indonesia.	(p. **20**)
2.	*P. sexstriatus*	*Holacanthus sexstriatus* Cuvier, 1831. Java, Indonesia.	(p. **23**)
3.	*P. xanthometopon*	*Holacanthus xanthometopon* Bleeker, 1853. Sumatra, Indonesia.	(p. **26**)
	Subgenus ***Pomacanthodes***		(p. **29**)
4.	*P. annularis*	*Chaetodon annularis* Bloch, 1787. East Indies.	(p. **30**)
5.	*P. asfur*	*Chaetodon asfur* Forsskal, 1775. Yemen, Red Sea.	(p. **40**)
6.	*P. chrysurus*	*Holacanthus chrysurus* Cuvier, 1831. Dorey Harbour, New Guinea.	(p. **33**)
7.	*P. imperator*	*Chaetodon imperator* Bloch, 1787. Japan.	(p. **34**)
8.	*P. maculosus*	*Chaetodon maculosus* Forsskal, 1775. Yemen, Red Sea.	(p. **42**)
9.	*P. rhomboides*	*Holacanthus rhomboides* Gilschrist & Thompson, 1908. Natal, South Africa.	(p. **38**)
10.	*P. semicirculatus*	*Holacanthus semicirculatus* Cuvier, 1831. Buru, Indonesia.	(p. **46**)
11.	*P. zonipectus*	*Pomacanthodes zonipectus* Gill, 1862. San Salvador, El Salvador.	(p. **50**)
	Subgenus ***Pomacanthus***		(p. **52**)
12.	*P. arcuatus*	*Chaetodon arcuatus* Linnaeus, 1758. Indiis.	(p. **54**)
13.	*P. paru*	*Chaetodon paru* Bloch, 1787. Brazil & Jamaica.	(p. **56**)

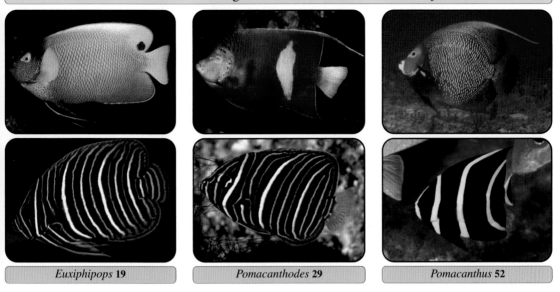

| *Euxiphipops* **19** | *Pomacanthodes* **29** | *Pomacanthus* **52** |

GENUS *Pomacanthus*, SUBGENUS *Euxiphipops* Fraser-Brunner, 1934

Masculine. Type species: *Holacanthus xanthometopon* Bleeker 1853. Replacement name for *Heteropyge* Fraser-Brunner 1933, previously used by *Heteropyge* Silvestri 1897 in Myriopoda. Comprises 3 species in the West Pacific. Characterised by 12–14 dorsal-fin spines; long ventral fin, filamentous in adults; scales moderately large; and median fins rounded. Juvenile patterns develop from 4 principal vertical stripes, one on head and 3 on body.

picture index to adults and juveniles

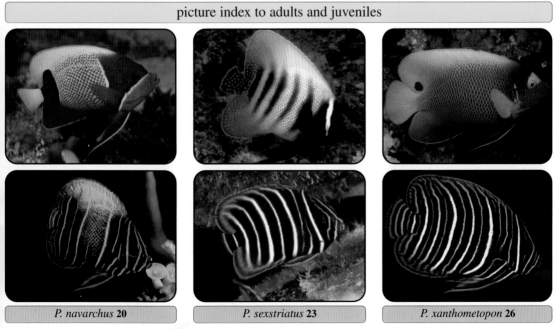

| *P. navarchus* **20** | *P. sexstriatus* **23** | *P. xanthometopon* **26** |

Blue-girdled Angelfish *Pomacanthus navarchus*

Holacanthus navarchus Cuvier 1831. Java.

Widespread Western Pacific, ranging into the Indian Ocean to Western Australia and Sumatra, northwards to the Philippines and Micronesia, and south to the Solomon Islands and northern Great Barrier Reef. Only common in outer reef habitats, coral rich lagoons and outer reef walls in a depth range of about 3 to 35 m. The Blue-girdled angel is generally shy and usually seen solitary, occasionally in pairs. Juveniles live in shallow and protected reef areas. The adults are mainly yellow-orange, including the dorsal and caudal fin, whilst the the head, pectorals and lower fins are deep blue, edged with a neon-blue. Juveniles are completely different in having numerous light blue vertical lines on a dark blue background. They are distinct from many similarly coloured angelfish juveniles (especially those of *P. annularis*) in having an orange dorsal, a transparent caudal, and a blue pectoral fin. Colour change to adult pattern begins early at a body length of about 5 to 8 cm. Length to 25 cm.

Remarks: known to hybridise with the Blue-faced angelfish. On one occasion the first author observed a Blue-girdled angelfish swimming together with an Emperor angelfish on an Indonesian reef, feeding on sponges and tunicates.

Aquarium: robust species, easy to maintain, and accepts most foods offered, especially when introduced as a small juvenile.

A   B

P. navarchus. **A** Flores, Indonesia. Length 22 cm. Rudie Kuiter. **B** aquarium. Juvenile stage. Frank Schneidewind.

C

P. navarchus. Rowley Shoals, WA, Australia. Depth 15 m. Length 20 cm. Rudie Kuiter.

D

P. navarchus. Flores, Indonesia. Adult pair at 25 m depth, lengths 22–24 cm. Rudie Kuiter.

P. navarchus. Flores, Indonesia. Subadult, still showing traces of the juvenile patterns. Length 15 cm. Depth 25 m. Rudie Kuiter.

E

P. navarchus. Flores, Indonesia. Adult pair at 20 m depth. Length about 22 cm. Rudie Kuiter.

Six-banded Angelfish *Pomacanthus sexstriatus*

Holacanthus sexstriatus Cuvier 1831. Java.

Ranges throughout the Indo-Australian Archipelago, reaching west to Thailand, east to the Solomon Islands and the Coral Sea and in the tropical zones of Japan and Australia. Occurs in a variety of habitats, from turbid lagoons to pristine outer reefs at a depth range between about 5 and 60 m. The species is usually shy, and encountered mainly in pairs. Juveniles live on shallower protected reefs. A distinct species with its pale body and six vertical dark stripes, and a dark head with a white vertical stripe. Juveniles are bluish black with vertical white lines on the body and head that change to blue on the fins. The colouration is similar to that of several other *Pomacanthus* juveniles, especially that of *P. xanthometopon*, but juvenile *P. sexstriatus* have a higher and more pointed dorsal, and a larger anal fin. The colouration changes at a length of about 10 cm. Length to 45 cm, common to 35 cm.

Remarks: scientific name, *sexstriatus*, meaning six stripes in relation to the dusky bands on the body. It may hybridise with *Pomacanthus xanthometopon*.

Aquarium: largest angelfish, growing too big for a normal home aquarium. However, it is durable, and socialises with other angelfish species, especially when kept as juveniles.

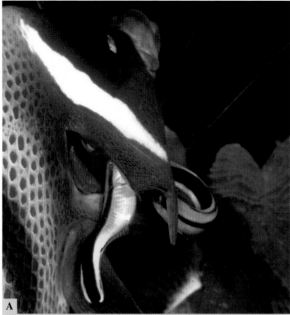

A

P. sexstriatus. A pair of cleaner wrasses, *Labroides dimidiatus*, checking for parasites in the angelfish's gill-cavity. Derawan, Indonesia. Depth 25 m. Length about 45 cm. Rudie Kuiter.

B

P. sexstriatus. Note the very long ventral fins. Derawan, Indonesia. Depth 25 m. Length about 45 cm. Rudie Kuiter.

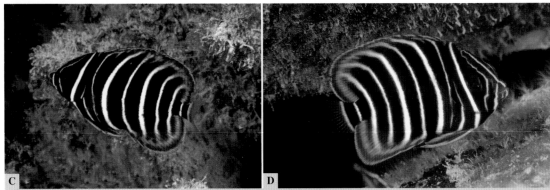

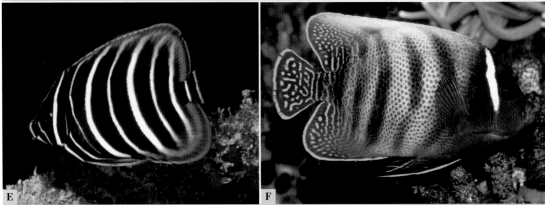

P. sexstriatus. Pulau Putri, Indonesia. Depth 3–4 m. **C** length 30 mm. **D** length 35 mm. Rudie Kuiter.

P. sexstriatus. **E** Pulau Putri, Indonesia. D. 3–4 m. L. 45 mm. **F** aquarium, losing its juvenile pattern, length 20 cm. Rudie Kuiter.

P. sexstriatus. Pair on the Great Barrier Reef, Australia. Depth 20 m. Length 35–40 cm. Rudie Kuiter.

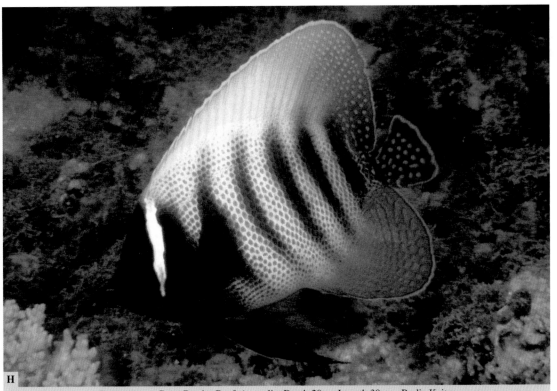

H

P. sexstriatus. Great Barrier Reef, Australia. Depth 20 m. Length 30 cm. Rudie Kuiter.

I

P. sexstriatus. Rowley Shoals, WA, Australia. Depth 12 m. Length 40 cm. Rudie Kuiter.

Indo-west Pacific. Western Pacific from southern Japan to Australia, ranging west into Indian Ocean to the Maldives and Thailand, and east to Vanuatu, Coral Sea. Adults live in coral rich lagoons and along outer reefs in a depth range of about 5 to 35 m. The Blue-faced angelfish is shy in most places and usually seen solitary, but occasionally it forms pairs which occupy large territories. This species feeds on sponges and tunicates, and makes loud bongo-like sounds when disturbed. Adults are readily identified by their brilliant blue head with an orange mask over the eyes, and have an obvious dark blue round spot on the end of the dorsal fin. Juveniles are bluish black with vertical blue and white lines, the lines being mainly straight on the body. Change from juvenile to adult pattern begins at a length of about 7 cm, and is usually completed when reaching 10 to 12 cm. Length to 40 cm, common to about 30 cm.

Remarks: it hybridises with its other *Euxiphipops* subgenera members, *Pomacanthus navarchus* & *P. sexstriatus*.

Aquarium: this species is quite hard to keep. Juveniles have the best chance to adapt to captivity and once established they are easily maintained.

P. xanthometopon. A not so shy individual in the Maldives. Some large individuals, like this one, are probably territorial males checking out intruders or possible threats. The image shows the diagnostic colouring on the head. Rudie Kuiter.

P. xanthometopon. Bali, Indonesia. Depth 25 m. Length about 36 cm. Rudie Kuiter.

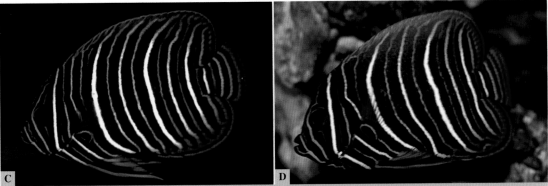

P. xanthometopon. **C** Pulau Putri, Indonesia. **D.** 4 m. L. 45 mm. Rudie Kuiter. **D** aquarium. Juvenile. Frank Schneidewind.

P. xanthometopon. With Moorish Idol and Giant Triggerfish. Halmahera, Indonesia. D. 18 m. Length ~32 cm. Helmut Debelius.

P. xanthometopon. Bali, Indonesia. Depth 25 m. Length about 35 cm. Rudie Kuiter.

P. xanthometopon. Pair, following a feeding hawksbill turtle and ready to pick up scraps. Sipadan, Malaysia. Doug Perrine.

GENUS *Pomacanthus*, SUBGENUS *Pomacanthodes* Gill, 1862

Masculine. Type species: *Pomacanthodes zonipectus* Gill, 1862. Comprises 8 species variously distributed in the Indo Pacific. Characterised by 11–14 dorsal-fin spines; median fins rounded to strongly pointed and dorsal fin often extended by filament in large adults. Juvenile patterns develop from 3 principal vertical stripes, often strongly and evenly curved to form half circles and even a full circle in one (*Pomacanthus imperator*).

picture index to adults

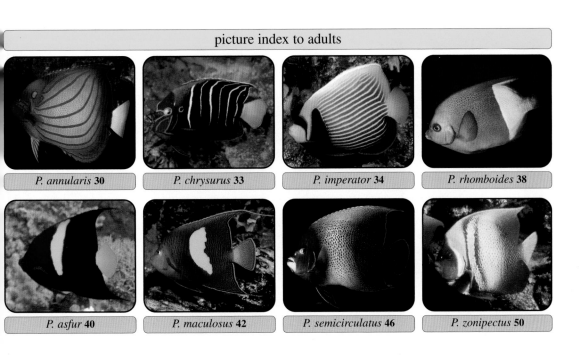

P. annularis 30	*P. chrysurus* 33	*P. imperator* 34	*P. rhomboides* 38
P. asfur 40	*P. maculosus* 42	*P. semicirculatus* 46	*P. zonipectus* 50

picture index to juveniles

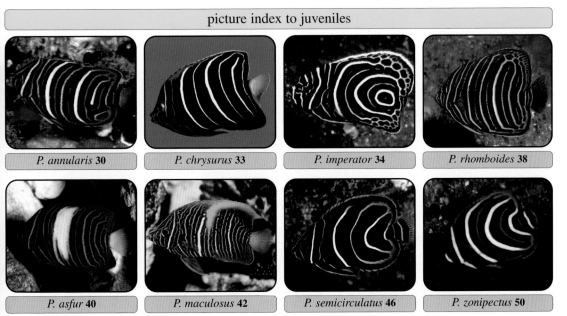

P. annularis 30	*P. chrysurus* 33	*P. imperator* 34	*P. rhomboides* 38
P. asfur 40	*P. maculosus* 42	*P. semicirculatus* 46	*P. zonipectus* 50

A

P. annularis. Similan Islands, Andaman Sea. Helmut Debelius.

Pomacanthus annularis Bloch 1787.
East Indies

Ranges from the west coast of India via Sri Lanka and Thailand to the southern Ryukyu Islands of Japan (north) and Indonesia to the Solomon Islands (east). It occurs in coastal reefs with sparse coral growth, prefers hiding places and often murky waters in depths of about 3 to 50 m, and it usually occurs singly or in pairs. Adults with brilliant blue curving stripes on its mostly olive body, and above the operculum its name-giving blue ring with olive inside. Dorsal develops a long elongated tip, reaching well over the caudal fin. Juveniles are bluish black with a light blue and white lined pattern. The juvenile pattern changes at a body length of about 10 cm. Length to 45 cm, usually 35 cm.

Remarks: records of *Pomacanthus annularis* from eastern Africa are based on misidentifications.

Aquarium: juveniles are easily kept, but this species grows to a large size.

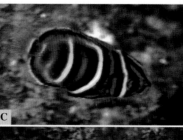

C

D

E

P. annularis. Juveniles. Bali, Indonesia.
Depth 1–2 m. Lengths: **C** 14 mm,
D 16 mm, **E** 20 mm. Rudie Kuiter.

B

P. annularis. Being cleaned by *Laroides dimidiatus*. Andaman Sea. Mark Strickland.

F

P. annularis. Pair, largest probably the male. Bali, Indonesia. Depth 25 m. Length 35–40 cm. Rudie Kuiter.

P. annularis. A large individual posing for the camera. Bali, Indonesia. Depth 25 m. Length 42 cm. Rudie Kuiter.

G

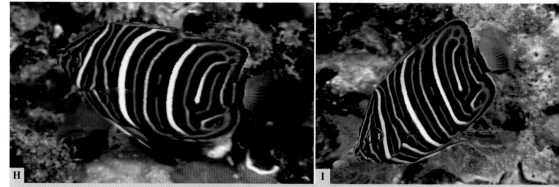

P. annularis. Bali, Indonesia. Depth 1 m. Length 50 mm. Rudie Kuiter.

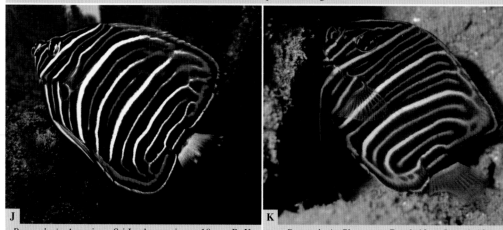

P. annularis. Aquarium, Sri Lanka specimen, 10 cm. R. K.

P. annularis. Singapore. Depth 10 m. Length 12 cm. R. K.

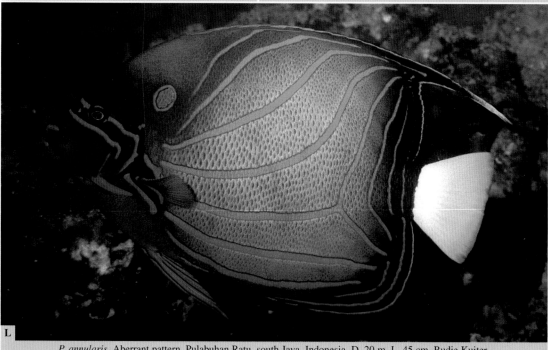

P. annularis. Aberrant pattern. Pulabuhan Ratu, south Java, Indonesia. D. 20 m. L. 45 cm. Rudie Kuiter.

Ear-spot Angelfish *Pomacanthus chrysurus*

Holacanthus chrysurus Cuvier 1831. No locality.

Western Indian Ocean, along the East African coast from Somalia south to KwaZulu-Natal. Recorded also from the Seychelles, Comoro Islands, and Madagascar. A solitary species found from shallow coastal reefs to offshore at depths to at least 30 m. An attractive and easily identified species at all stages. It has distinct white vertical lines on a dark body and yellow caudal fin. The head has a pattern of irridescent blue lines and the "ear-spot" behind the head shown in adults gives it its common name. Called Gold-tail angelfish in South Africa. Length. to 30 cm.

Remarks: the type-locality given for this species is New Guinea, and since that species is not known from there, this is clearly in error. The type specimen is housed in the Paris Museum and clearly is this species. In addition its description also clearly applies to this species. *Pomacanthus chrysurus* hybridises with *P. maculosus,* a rare expatriate from the Arabian Seas in which, in its larval stage it is transported by favourable

A

P. chrysurus. Aldabra, Seychelles. D. 5 m. L. 24 cm. Helmut Debelius.

currents into the geographical range of *P. chrysurus*.

Aquarium: the ear-spot angelfish is a popular aquarium fish and in high demand in Europe. It is relatively easy to keep.

B

C

P. chrysurus. Aquarium. Juveniles. **B** 40 mm. **C** 75 mm. Frank Schneidewind.

D

P. chrysurus. Kenya. Depth 12 m. Length 22 cm. Jerry Allen.

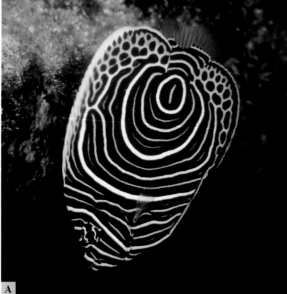

Emperor Angelfish *Pomacanthus imperator*
Pomacanthus imperator Bloch 1787, Japan.

The most widespread angelfish, known from the Red Sea and western Indian Ocean east to Polynesia and Hawaii in the central Pacific. However, only one specimen suspected to have been released by a local ornamental fish importer is known from Hawaii and there are some geographical variations. Lives in coral rich lagoons and outer reefs from 3 to 70 m, where the Emperor angelfish is usually encountered singly or in pairs. Adults are blue with diagonal narrow yellow lines; the eyes are covered by a mask-like dark band and they have a yellow caudal fin. Juveniles are completely different in colour, being almost black with white and blue curving lines, forming circles near the caudal base which distinguishes them from similar species. Colour change to the adult pattern starts at a length of about 8 cm. Males grow about 20% longer than females and the stripe hiding the eye in all specimens is basically dark blue in males, but light bluish grey in females. During spawning the colours and the striped body flank pattern of the female fades and the pair generate loud, low frequency, drum-like sounds from their swimbladder. Length to 40 cm, usually to 30 cm.

A
P. imperator. Maldives. Depth 25 m. Length 10 cm. Rudie Kuiter.

B
P. imperator. Its gills being cleaned by *Lysmata* cleaner shrimp and *Labroides* cleaner wrasse. Andaman Sea. Mark Strickland.

Remarks: the Emperor Angelfish is one of the best known members of the family. However, there are some differences in the Indian- and Pacific Ocean populations. Most obvious is the rounded posterior end of the dorsal fin in the Indian Ocean population rather than pointed (extended by a filament in large adults) in the Pacific populations.

Aquarium: easily kept and long-lived. In the Nancy Tropical Aquarium an Emperor angel lived for 15 years. Juveniles adapt easily to captivity, but usually this species becomes dominant and aggressive to other aquarium inmates when getting bigger. The Emperor Angelfish should not be kept together with sessile invertebrates like living soft or hard corals.

C

P. imperator. Tuvalu, South Pacific. Depth 15 m. Length 30 cm. Helmut Debelius.

D

P. imperator. Flores, Indonesia. Depth 25 m. Pair in habitat. The larger individual is usually the male. Rudie Kuiter.

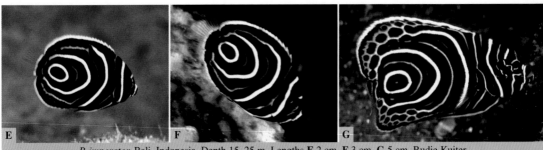

P. imperator. Bali, Indonesia. Depth 15–25 m. Lengths **E** 2 cm, **F** 3 cm, **G** 5 cm. Rudie Kuiter.

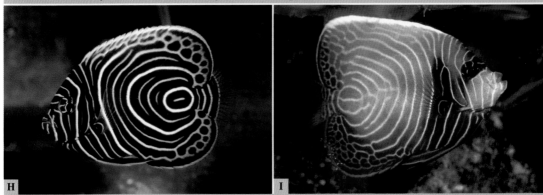

P. imperator. Indonesia. **H** Bali. D. 25 m. L. 8 cm. **I** cleaner shrimp on anal fin. Flores. D. 20 m. L. 12 cm. Rudie Kuiter.

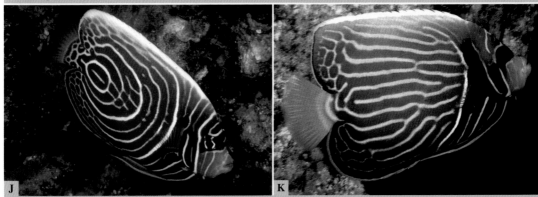

P. imperator. **J** Flores, Indonesia. Depth 15 m. Length 14 cm. **K** Guam. Depth 3 m. Length 15 cm. Rudie Kuiter.

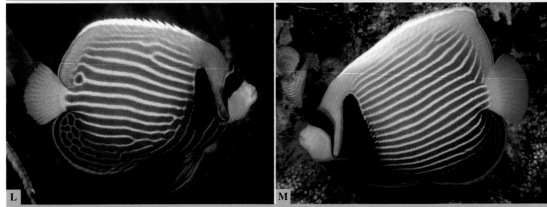

P. imperator. **L** Bali, Indonesia. D. 25 m. L. 16 cm. **M** Great Barrier Reef, Australia. D. 15 m. L. 20 cm. Rudie Kuiter.

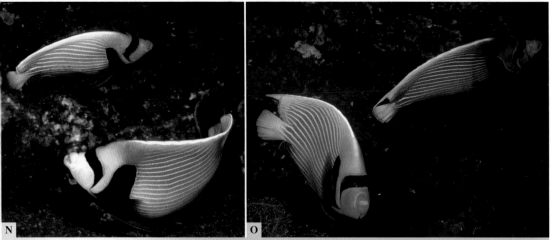

P. imperator. Bali, Indonesia. Depth 10–12 m. Adult pairs, **N** Indian form. **O** Pacific form. Rudie Kuiter.

P. imperator. Adult pair. Egypt, Red Sea. Depth 15 m. Helmut Debelius.

P. imperator. Adult chasing juveniles out of its territory. Mauritius. Depth 22 m. Helmut Debelius.

P. rhomboides. Juvenile stage. Length 5 cm. Dennis King.

Old Woman Angelfish
Pomacanthus rhomboides

Holacanthus rhomboides Gilschrist & Thompson, 1908. Natal, South Africa

Only known from Western Indian Ocean, from South Africa to Mozambique, and not further north as sometimes reported (see *remarks*). Adults on offshore reefs at depths to at least 30 m, whilst juveniles are inshore on shallow reefs and in rock pools. Adults are usually in small loose groups and may congregate above reefs in loose groups to feed on plankton in the open water high above the seabed, even at the surface, in pursuit of food (**E**). They also feed on a great variety of sessile invertebrates. Adult is rather friendly towards divers, and may come 0,to investigate. This species has a deep body and angular dorsal and anal fins. Adult specimens may develop a small bump on the forehead. *Pomacanthus rhomboides* is a rather drab member of the genus, being mostly grey with a whitish or pale-blue triangular patch over the posterior third of its body. The juvenile stage is like the other *Pomacanthus*-juveniles, and especially similar to *P. annularis,* with blue vertical lines on a dark background. Length to 46 cm.

Remarks: Rüppells description of a Red Sea juvenile *Pomacanthus maculosus,* as *P. striatus* in 1835, has led to confusion with the juvenile of this species and its distribution. Records of *P. annularis* from South Africa are probably based on juvenile *P. rhomboides.*

Aquarium: an easily kept species, but it grows large. Due to its drabness, there is little demand for it in the aquarium trade and only seen regularly on display in South African public aquariums.

P. rhomboides. A–C Aliwal Shoal, south of Durban, South Africa. **B & C** subadult losing juvenile colours. Rudie Kuiter.

D *P. rhomboides.* Aliwal Shoal, south of Durban, South Africa. Depth 25 m. Large, about 45 cm. Rudie Kuiter.

E *P. rhomboides.* Aliwal Shoal, south of Durban, South Africa. Large adults feeding on plankton, high above the reef. Dennis King.

Crescent Angelfish *Pomacanthus asfur*
Chaetodon asfur Forsskål 1775. Red Sea

Red Sea from Hurghada south, ranging into the western Gulf of Aden, but not reaching the coast of Oman. A solitary and usually shy species, inhabiting protected shallow lagoon reefs to about 20 m depth, preferring the silty water of muddy reefs where visibility is often poor. Adults are iridescent blue and black with a bright yellow band from just above the anus into the dorsal fin, and yellow caudal fin. Juveniles have alternating thin blue and white vertical lines. With growth, a yellow bar develops centrally on the body below the dorsal fin and above the abdomen, changing gradually to the adult stage at a length of about 4–6 cm. Length to 40 cm, but usually to 25 cm.

Remarks: most books illustrated *Pomacanthus maculosus* as the juvenile *P. asfur*, simply because it is much more common and has a yellow band and caudal fin. *P. asfur* juveniles are distinguished from *P. maculosus* in having a more vertical and more forward placed yellow bar, often pale in small juveniles, and also the anal fin is much more angular at comparable sizes. Both may have a yellow tail and this is not helpful in distinguishing the two as is often suggested. Adult *P. asfur* and *P. maculosus* were seen together, but no hybrids have been reported so far. An aberrant morph is known in which the band and caudal fin are white instead of yellow.

P. asfur. Aquarium. Subadult. Helmut Debelius.

Aquarium: apart from its brilliant colours the crescent angelfish is a true beauty with its long dorsal and anal filaments. Once adapted, *Pomacanthus asfur* is a hardy pet. An adult specimen was kept by author H.D. for almost 3 years, together with 2 other angelfishes (*Holacanthus*) and 2 spiny lobsters, until it had grown too big and was donated to the Frankfurt public aquarium.

P. asfur. Aquarium. Juvenile, same individual that grew to adult stage. Length 35 & 45 mm. Kohsuke Imabayashi.

P. asfur swimming with *P. maculosus*, a behaviour observed only once. Jeddah, Saudi Arabia, Red Sea. Helmut Debelius.

E

P. asfur. Safaga, Egypt, northern limit of its range. Helmut Debelius.

F

P. asfur. Aquarium. Adult. Length 25 cm. Helmut Debelius.

Yellow-blotch Angelfish *Pomacanthus maculosus*

Chaetodon maculosus Forsskål 1775. Red Sea.

Throughout the Red Sea to the western tip of the Arabian (Persian) Gulf, and ranges southward to the coasts of Somalia and Kenya. Mainly occurs on sandy or coral rich reefs, shallow depths to at least 60 m. The yellow-blotch angelfish lives solitary, establishing large territories in fringing reefs, which are constantly patrolled. A large and impressive angelfish due to its shape and colour. Adults usually pale blue with a large yellow blotch on their sides. Blotch colour may fade or darken with mood. *Pomacanthus maculosus* is sometimes confused with *P. asfur*, but this species has a yellow caudal fin as well. Small juvenile *P. maculosus* have alternating white and light blue vertical lines on a dark background, and are distinguished from the similar juvenile *P. asfur* by their paler caudal fin and more rounded anal fin, but the caudal fin may also turn bright yellow at some stage. Changes from juvenile to adult patterns occur at a length of about 10 cm. Can reach 50 cm, usually to about 35 cm.

P. maculosus. Large adult feeding in a seagrass bed. Egypt, Red Sea. Depth 3 m. Length 45 cm. Rudie Kuiter.

P. maculosus. The normally yellow blotch darkened. Egypt, Red Sea. Depth 5 m. Length 42 cm. Rudie Kuiter.

Remarks: *Pomacanthus maculosus* is rare in Kenya and when a species cannot find a partner it often pairs with its closest relative, *P. chrysurus,* producing hybrids.

Aquarium: very robust and docile angelfish. They used to be imported on a regular basis from Yemen to Europe as tiny juveniles, but are now exported from Hong Kong or Taiwan where they are aquacultured. They grow quickly and adults are best kept in either very large or public aquariums.

C

D

P. maculosus. **C** small juvenile in aquarium. **D** adult grazing algae from dead coral. Helmut Debelius.

E

P. maculosus. Diver admiring a pair of large individuals. Gulf of Suez, Egypt, Red Sea. Helmut Debelius.

F

P. maculosus. In cleaning station, changing its blotch to black. Egypt, Red Sea. Depth 5 m. Length 42 cm. Helmut Debelius.

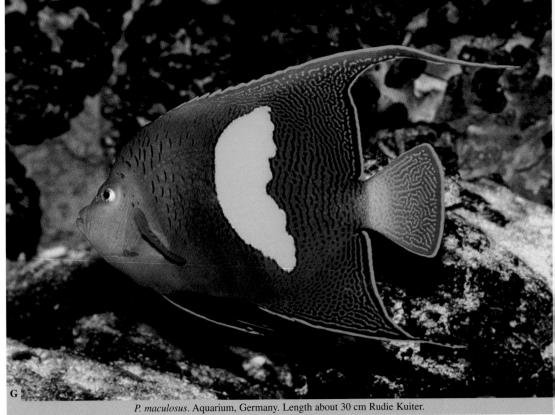

G

P. maculosus. Aquarium, Germany. Length about 30 cm Rudie Kuiter.

Yellow-blotch Angelfish *Pomacanthus maculosus* in Japan and the south China Seas

P. maculosus. Juveniles from Hong Kong. **A** yellow blotch starting to develop. **B** dorsal becoming pointed. Hiroyuki Tanaka.

The occurrence of what is almost certainly *Pomacanthus maculosus,* from the Red Sea and Arabian Sea, in Japanese waters for several decades (first in 1960) is somewhat of a mystery. Specimens have appeared intermittently in the southwestern parts of Japan, with some individuals observed by divers in a particular place for several months. It has been suggested that it may be an introduced species from aquarists' releases or was transported in its early larval stage in the ballast water of ships. Latter is highly unlikely as no other individuals of this family have appeared in areas where exotics from other families, such as gobies, are known. In addition the ships coming from the native region of *P. maculosus* are fully loaded and do not bring ballast water. The release of aquarium fishes is the most likely scenario, especially after learning from Keith Wilson, a Hong Kong fish-enthusiast, that Buddhists often buy expensive fish to give them their freedom (as well as birds, turtles, etc, and even, unfortunately releasing freshwater turtles in the sea!!). It is quite possible that a breeding population of *P. maculosus* is now established somewhere in the region. We know that this species expatriates over great distances, carried in their larval stage by currents. This would explain the intermittent and irregular occurrence of this species in southern Japan.

P. maculosus. Large juvenile. Aquarium. Scott Michael.

It is also known that importers may release sick or damaged specimens into their local waters (for many· years), causing records of species well away from their normal geographical range (such as *Pomacanthus imperator* in Hawaiian waters).

P. maculosus. Subadult. Nichinan coast, Miyazaki, Japan. Depth 6–7 m. Length 25 cm. Akihiko Shinchi.

Semicircle Angelfish
Pomacanthus semicirculatus

Holacanthus semicirculatus Cuvier 1831. Indonesia.

Widespread Indo-west Pacific, from East Africa to Fiji, north to Chiba Pref., Japan and south to central NSW, Australia. Occurs on mixed coral or rocky coastal reefs from intertidal to at least 40 m depth. The species is hardly shy in most places, and usually seen singly, very rarely in pairs. Juveniles are cryptic when very small and usually in algae-rich crevices at depths of 1 or 2 m. Adults have electric-blue opercular margins and fin margins that adorn the brownish green body. Juveniles are totally different in colour with backward-curving vertical blue and white lines, which are almost semicircular on the posterior third of the body. In the Western Indian Ocean this angelfish is also called "Koran angelfish" due to the Arabic script-like pattern on the median fins of large juveniles. Colouration changes from juvenile to adult patterns start at a body length of about 10 cm. Length to 40 cm, common to about 30 cm.

P. semicirculatus. Bali, Indonesia. Length 12 cm. Rudie Kuiter.

Remarks: this species emits loud audible noises when threatened or excited. *Pomacanthus semicirculatus* may hybridise with *P. maculosus* in Kenya. The author HD watched a Semicircle angel swimming together with an Emperor angel as if they were a pair for more than 40 minutes in the Seychelles, in shallow water, feeding together from reef patch to reef patch even crossing wide sandy areas. However, this may simply be companionship.

Aquarium: this species is easy to maintain and is recommended for beginners. In captivity the fishes reach a length of 20 to 25 cm. Keeping *Pomacanthus semicirculatus* with invertebrates is not advisable. It should be kept only in a fish-community tank.

P. semicirculatus. Derawan, Indonesia Depth 30 m. Length 35 cm. Rudie Kuiter.

P. semicirculatus. Derawan, Indonesia Depth 30 m. Length 35 cm. Rudie Kuiter.

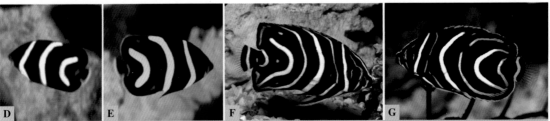

P. semicirculatus. Aquarium. Sydney, Australia. From 2–4 m. Lengths **D** 10 mm, **E** 12 mm, **F** 22 mm, **G** 25 mm. Rudie Kuiter.

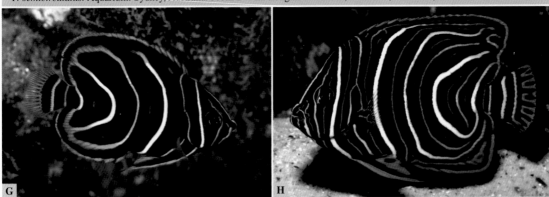

P. semicirculatus. **G** Flores, Indonesia. D. 3 m. L. 30 mm. **H** Aquarium. Moreton Bay, Australia. From 5 m L. 8 cm. Rudie Kuiter.

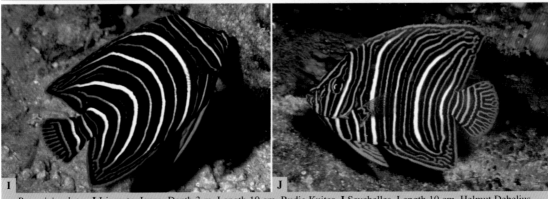

P. semicirculatus. **I** Iriomote, Japan. Depth 3 m. Length 10 cm. Rudie Kuiter. **J** Seychelles. Length 10 cm. Helmut Debelius.

P. semicirculatus. **K** Aquarium, Indian Ocean subadult. **L** Rowley Shoals, WA, Australia. D. 20 m. L. 25 cm. Rudie Kuiter.

P. semicirculatus. Kerama, Japan. Depth 25 m. Length 25 cm. Rudie Kuiter.

P. semicirculatus. Typical Indian Ocean colours. Mauritius. Depth 18 m. Length ~26 cm. Helmut Debelius.

A

P. zonipectus. Adult pair. Sea of Cortez. Helmut Debelius.

Pomacanthodes zonipectus Gill 1862. El Salvador.

Tropical eastern Pacific, from the Gulf of California south to Peru, the Galápagos and mexican Revilla Gigedos Islands. Occurs in rocky and coral habitats at depths between 5 and 30 m. The Cortez angelfish either lives singly, in pairs and may also form aggregations. The author HD dived in the Sea of Cortez several times and saw the adults in pairs only, whilst the juveniles were solitary. Adults are dark in appearance and have a large yellow area reaching from the forehead to the breast. There is a broad sickle-shaped body stripe behind the pectoral fins. Juveniles are very similarly patterned to juveniles of *Pomacanthus semicirculatus*, but the semicircular lines of this species are yellow rather than white as in juvenile *P. paru* and *P. arcuatus* from the western Atlantic. Length to 45 cm.

Remarks: judging by the colouration of the juvenile, body shape of the adult, and behaviour, *Pomacanthus zonipectus* seems closely related to the 2 Caribbean *Pomacanthus*-species. The Atlantic species were isolated from the Pacific 3 to 4 million years ago by the rise of the Central American land bridge.

Aquarium: the Cortez Angelfish is on display in many public aquaria on the Californian coast. It feeds on sessile invertebrates and algae, and usually readily accepts substitute food. A long-lived species that grows rather slowly. Some authors recommend the lower temperature of their range for the aquarium, and suggest a susceptibility to diseases.

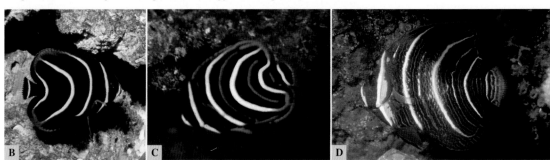

B   C   D

P. zonipectus. Juvenile stages. Sea of Cortez. Depths 8–18 m. Helmut Debelius.

E

P. zonipectus. Adult pair. Sea of Cortez. Depth 22 m. Helmut Debelius.

P. zonipectus. Large adult. Sea of Cortez. Depth 15 m. Helmut Debelius.

Masculine. Type species: *Chaetodon arcuatus* Linnaeus 1758. Represented by 2 Atlantic species. Has 9 or 10 dorsal-fin spines (11–14 in other subgenera of *Pomacanthus*); anal fin angular and produced into long filament in adults. The two species are very similar in shape, in *P. arcuatus* caudal fin is truncate and in *P. paru* it is much more rounded. Adult *P. arcuatus* are pale to dusky with dark spots, whilst *P. paru* are darker and have pale spots. Juveniles are best distinguished by their caudal fin patterns as shown below.

picture index to adults and juveniles

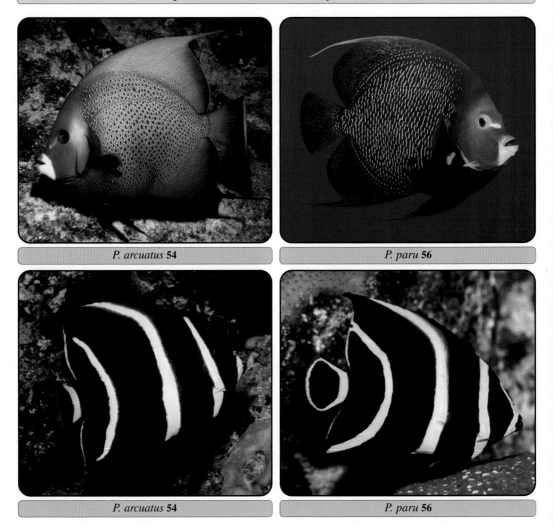

P. arcuatus **54**

P. paru **56**

P. arcuatus **54**

P. paru **56**

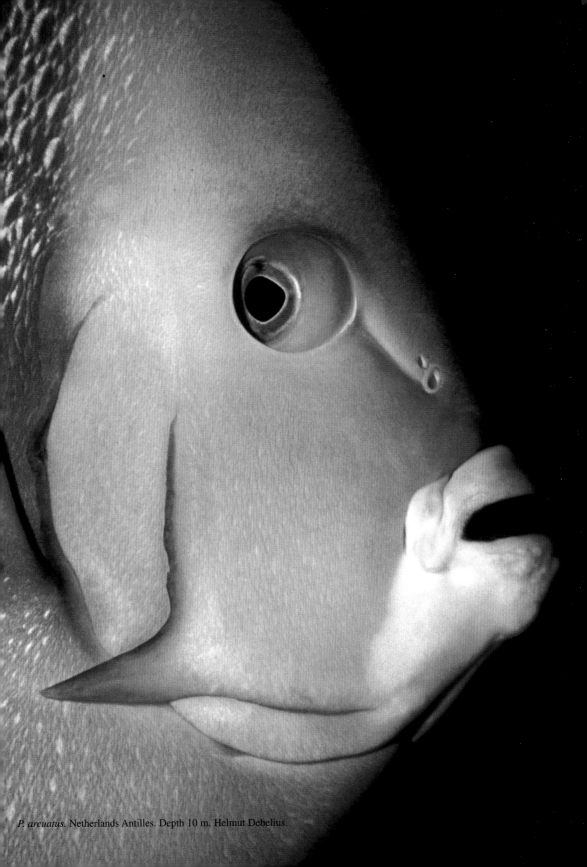

P. arcuatus. Netherlands Antilles. Depth 10 m. Helmut Debelius.

Grey Angelfish *Pomacanthus arcuatus*

Chaetodon arcuatus Linnaeus 1758.

Tropical western Atlantic, common in Florida, Bahamas, the Gulf of Mexico and the Caribbean. North to the Bermudas, even as far as New York, and ranging south to Brazil to the major barrier for Caribbean fishes: the freshwater outflow from the Amazon. Found on shallow coral and rocky reefs to about 30 m depth. The Grey angelfish are usually in pairs and readily approach divers. They feed on a variety of sponges, corals, tunicates and algae. This species occasionally congregates in large aggregations to feed on plankton as well during an algae bloom. Juveniles inhabit shallow patch reefs and grassy areas. Juvenile *Pomacanthus arcuatus* have been observed cleaning larger fishes. The adults are uniformly grey and each scale has a black dot. The inner side of the pectoral fin is bright yellow. The soft dorsal and anal fins of adults are produced into filaments. The attractive juvenile colouration is black with pale yellow bands, one on the caudal-fin base, three on the body, and one extending down from the forehead and across the mouth to the chin. Length to 50 cm, usually about 35 cm.

Remarks: the Grey angelfish is regarded as a food fish in some areas, its biology is similar to that of *Pomacanthus paru,* and both swim with short, straight motions.

Aquarium: this species is easy to keep and is regarded as one of the hardiest angelfish species, but it grows much too large for the normal home aquarium. It also nips at invertebrates, making it unsuitable for a living-reef aquarium. Reproduction in captivity has been achieved artificially by taking and mixing gametes from the parents.

A

P. arcuatus. Subadult. Florida Keys. Depth 10 m. Length 26 cm. Roger Steene.

P. arcuatus. Juvenile stages, and adult aggregation during an algae bloom. Bahamas. **B–D** Doug Perrine.

P. arcuatus. Adult. Abrolhos Reefs, Brazil. Osmar Luiz-Júnior.

Chaetodon paru Bloch 1787. Brazil & Jamaica.

Widespread tropical Western and Central Atlantic, ranging from the Caribbean north to Florida and the Bermudas, and south almost along the entire Brazilian coast to the latitude of 30°S, south of Rio de Janeiro (Joyeux, Floeter, Ferreira and Gasparini, 2001). Expatriates reach the central Atlantic island Ascension. It lives on shallow coral reefs, algae and rubble areas, but ranges into deep water and reported to 100 m. The French Angelfish has a large, discus-shaped body with posteriorly pointed dorsal and anal fins that elongate with age. Adults are dark grey, highlighting the yellow scale-margins as a series of vertical dashes. It has a yellow cheek-spine and yellow around the eye and a yellow blotch at the base of the pectoral fin. The head is usually a paler grey than the body. Juveniles are black with yellow bands, one forming a loop on the caudal fin, three on the body and one on the nape and mouth to the chin. Length to 40 cm.

Remarks: distinguished from the similar *Pomacanthus arcuatus* by its rounder caudal fin and different colour pattern on that fin when juvenile (yellow fin with yellow margin around most of it, forming a loop, which is lacking in *P. arcuatus*).

Aquarium: robust species, readily accepts substitute food, can be maintained with luck as a pair. *Pomacanthus paru* is highly recommended for beginners. Reproduction of the French angelfish in captivity has been achieved artificially by taking and mixing gametes from the parents, and exports are widespread.

A

P. paru. Large juvenile. Bonaire. Depth 12 m. Length 18 cm. Roger Steene.

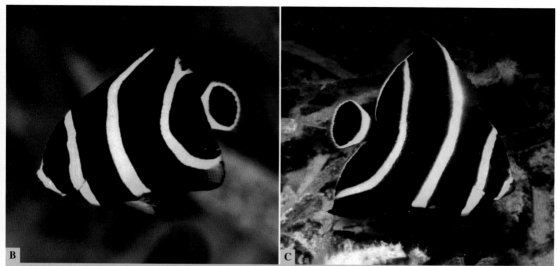

P. paru. Juvenile stages. **B** Cayman Island. Depth 3 m. Length 3 cm. **C** Bonaire. Depth 10 m. Length 15 cm. Roger Steene.

P. paru. Large adult. Cayman Island. Depth 12 m. Length 35 cm. Roger Steene.

E
P. paru. Subadult. Antigua. D. 15 m. L. 15 cm. Helmut Debelius.

F
G
P. paru. **F** juvenile. Laje de Santos I., Brazil. Osmar Luiz-Júnior. **G** small juvenile cleaning goatfish. Jan Post.

H
P. paru. Adult pair in seagrass habitat. Bahamas. Depth 8 m. Helmut Debelius.

P. paru. Large adult. Antigua. Depth 20 m. Length 42 cm. Helmut Debelius.

GENUS *Holacanthus* Lacepéde, 1802

Masculine. Type species: *Chaetodon tricolor* Bloch, 1795. The genus *Holacanthus* comprises 7 species, presently divided into 3 subgenera: *Plitops,* with 3 species living at very remote islands in the eastern Pacific; *Angelichthys,* also with 3 species in the Caribbean, and both sides of the Atlantic Ocean; and *Holacanthus* with a single species confined to the western Atlantic. The various members have relatively small geographical distributions, and most are specialised feeders, primarily targeting sponges. Some of them take on the role of cleaners for a time, removing troublesome parasites from various other fishes, including sharks. This behaviour varies between juveniles and adults and between different localities or populations of the same species. The adults may occupy large territories either solitary or in pairs. In remote ocean outposts, some species form school-like aggregations, especially the populations of *H. clarionensis* and *H. passer.* At certain locations in the Caribbean *H. tricolor* is found in small groups of females and a dominating male, in a harem-like arrangement. All species go through remarkable colour changes on their way to adulthood, so juveniles can look completely different from the adults. The various members of *Holacanthus* range in maximum length from 25 to 45 cm, and are amongst the largest fishes in the family Pomacanthidae.

The members of *Holacanthus* are popular amongst aquarists in North America, Japan and Europe. They are found widespread in public aquariums and often on display are the large and beautifully marked ones from the west Atlantic. Due to their special diet, like most angelfishes, they are not always easy to maintain although juveniles are generally more adaptable and can be accommodated more quickly than adults. Some species are very sensitive concerning transportation (*H. ciliaris*), others are quite aggressive towards inmates (*H. passer*), and generally not suitable for a reef aquarium full of invertebrates, as the large growing angelfishes nip at soft and hard corals.

List of subgenera and species.

	Subgenus *Angelichthys*		(p. **64**)
1.	*H. africanus*	*Holacanthus africanus* Cadenat, 1950. Senegal.	(p. **66**)
2.	*H. bermudensis*	*Holacanthus bermudensis* Goode, 1876. No locality.	(p. **74**)
3.	*H. ciliaris*	*Chaetodon ciliaris* (Linnaeus, 1758. W. Atlantic/Carribean.	(p. **68**)
	Subgenus *Holacanthus*		(p. **61**)
4.	*H. tricolor*	*Chaetodon tricolor* Bloch, 1795. Brazil.	(p. **61**)
	Subgenus *Plitops*		(p. **76**)
5.	*H. clarionensis*	*Holacanthus clarionensis* Gilbert, 1890. Clarion I., w. Mexico.	(p. **80**)
6.	*H. limbaughi*	*Holacanthus limbaughi* Baldwin, 1963. Clipperton I., e. Pacific.	(p. **82**)
7.	*H. passer*	*Holacanthus passer* Valenciennes, 1846. Galápagos.	(p. **78**)

GENUS *HOLACANTHUS* - Subgenera Picture Index to adults and juveniles

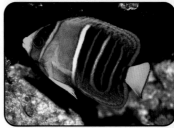

| *Holacanthus* **61** | *Angelichthys* **64** | *Plitops* **76** |

Masculine. Type species: *Chaetodon tricolor* Bloch, 1795. The subgenus *Holacanthus* comprises a single species in the western Atlantic, however, the populations between Brazil and the Carribean are genetically slightly different.

Rock Beauty *Holacanthus tricolor*

Chaetodon tricolor Bloch 1795. Brazil.

Tropical western and south-eastern Atlantic: from the Bermudas to Georgia, mainland U.S.A., and into the Gulf of Mexico, the Caribbean Sea and along the Brazilian coast south to its remote island of Trindade. Inhabits seaweed-covered shallow reef platforms to outer reefs to depths of about 90 m. Adults feed almost exclusively on the sponges encrusted on the rocks (up to 99%). The rock beauties normally occur in pairs, but also form harem-like small groups defended by the male who claims a territory. Spawns during dusk, and normally in the few days leading up to full moon. Whilst the males may spawn with several females in one session, the females participate only once. The adult rock beauty is readily identified by the unmistakable black and yellow colouration. Anterior third of body and caudal fin yellow, rest of body black. Also conspicuous are its blue lips and the blue upper and lower part of the eye. Small juveniles are brilliantly yellow, and have a large blue-ringed ocellus near the caudal fin. This ocellus expands during growth, and gives rise to the typical black colouration. Amongst pairs the male is typically larger than the female, which becomes obvious while watching rock beauties on the reef. Length to 30 cm.

Aquarium: adults often refuse substitute food and unfortunately nip at invertebrates in the reef aquarium. Although this splendid fish usually stays small in captivity, it is generally aggressive towards other inmates and also often misses out when having to compete for food, so careful selection is required.

A

H. tricolor. A perfect example of an adult. Escalvada I., Brazil. Depth 13 m. Length 25 cm. Sergio Floeter.

H. tricolor. Caribbean. **B** Bimini. Length 4 cm. Paul Humann. **C** St. Vincent. Depth 8 m. Length 5 cm. Roger Steene.

H. tricolor. Bonaire, Netherlands Antilles. Depth 15 m. Length 15 cm. Roger Steene.

H. tricolor. Escavalda I., Brazil. Adult pair. Depth 18 m. Length 12 & 20 cm. João Gasparini.

H. tricolor. **F** Aquarium. Length 12 cm. Rudie Kuiter. **G** Curacao. Netherlands Antilles. Length 12 cm. M. Runge.

H. tricolor. Bahamas. Sharing habitat with *H. ciliaris* and a juvenile *Pomacanthus paru* working as a cleaner. Helmut Debelius.

GENUS *Holacanthus,* SUBGENUS *Angelichthys* Jordan & Evermann, 1896

Masculine. Type species: *Chaetodon ciliaris* Bloch, 1795. The subgenus *Angelichthys* comprises 3 Atlantic species, 2 on the western and one on the eastern side of the Atlantic Ocean.

Species Picture Index to adults and juveniles

H. africanus **66**   *H. ciliaris* **68**   *H. bernudensis* **74**

Holacanthus africanus. Collected at the Cape Verde Islands, at home in my aquarium. Helmut Debelius.

My *Holacanthus africanus* expedition

Helmut Debelius proudly pointing at his prize-catch *Holacanthus africanus* (left fish).

Since its description in 1950, mystery surrounded this angelfish from the west African coast, and only b&w photos of a dead specimen existed in the Frankfurt Senckenberg Museum.

In December 1975 I grabbed the opportunity of participating in the first trip organised by a travel agent to the Cape Verde Islands, and getting the chance to collect the West African Angelfish *Holacanthus africanus* for my home aquarium. Soon I was enjoying some quite adventurous dives from primitive fishing boats and, more importantly, was in pursuit of fishes with my hand net. I succeeded in collecting a good selection of aquarium fishes, including several endemic butterflyfishes, damsels and my goal: a juvenile *H. africanus*. This jewel was kept in a plastic drum and the water was changed regularly until the time came to return to Germany. The fishes were packed in plastic bags without any insulation and carried as hand luggage on to the airplane. However, during the scheduled overnight stop in Lisbon the very cold winter temperatures cooled the water inside the plastic bags, and became too cold for the fishes. To fix this problem, I filled the bath-tub in the hotel and sat together with my fish in the warm tub until it was time to catch the plane to Frankfurt early next morning. All Cape Verde fishes survived this stress and I kept them for almost 15 months, until I went to Jordan's Gulf of Aqaba for one year. *H. africanus* did very well in my aquarium, and was easy to maintain, taking a particular liking to frozen shrimps. Keeping it at a temperature of 25°C, considerably higher than around the Cape Verde Islands, didn't seem to bother this angelfish at all.

This West African Angelfish became the star of the living rare coral-fishes display in the Senckenberg Museum. Aquarists from all over Europe came to see the first ever living specimen shown in captivity.

West African Angelfish
Holacanthus africanus

Holacanthus africanus Cadenat 1951.
Gorée, Senegal.

West African coast of the eastern Atlantic
ranging from the equatorial waters off Kongo
north to Senegal and the Cape Verde Islands.
Inhabits very shallow rocky areas and sandy
seabeds to a depth of at least 50 m. Adults have
a relatively uniform brownish olive colour, the
central area of the body somewhat paler, and
feature a large ocellate 'ear'-spot. Juveniles
display a totally different pattern and up to a
length of about 4 cm they have a brilliantly
orange-yellow caudal fin, and a shining blue
stripe in the middle of the body as well as two
narrow blue bars in front and behind the eye. At
a length of about 5 cm the juveniles begin to
change to the adult colours: a sickle-shaped
lighter zone appears behind the pectoral fin, the
blue colouration fades, and a yellowish brown
one dominates. At a length of about 10 cm the
fish have the complete adult colouration. Males
grow larger than females, and have a broader
pale area centrally on the body. Length to 40
cm.

Remarks: Holacanthus africanus is the only
member of the family Pomacanthidae in the
eastern Atlantic

H. africanus. Saõ Tomé. Depth 20 m. Length 15 cm. Peter Wirtz.

H. africanus. Cape Verde Islands. Depth 15 m. Length 30 cm. Helmut Debelius.

H. africanus. **C** aquarium, from Ghana L. 25 mm. Roger Lubbock. **D** Cape Verde Is. D. 5 m. L. 40 mm. Helmut Debelius.

H. africanus. **E** Gulf of Guinea. D. 10 m. L. 6 cm. Roger Steene. **F** aquarium, same as below, when first introduced.

H. africanus. **F & G** aquarium. From Cape Verde Is. **F** length 5 cm. **G** length 7 cm, after 6 weeks. Helmut Debelius.

Chaetodon ciliaris Linnaeus 1758. W. Atlantic/Caribbean.

Western Atlantic, from Florida, the Bahamas and the Caribbean (25°N) south to Brazil, ranging to the subtropical area off Rio de Janeiro (27°S). Adults usually offshore, inhabiting rubble areas of shallow to deep reefs, at depths between about 5 to 60 m. They occur either singly or in pairs, but observed in the southern Caribbean in small groups in a typical harem-like arrangement in which a male claims a territory in which he has a small number of females. Juveniles are solitary and live in shallow habitats, including mangroves, and often perform as cleaners. A conspicuously coloured species, regarded by many to be one of the most beautiful angelfishes. Adults feature a dark blue spot on forehead, speckled and ringed with brilliant blue, which forms the "crown", which may fade a bit in older Queen angelfish individuals. The paired and caudal fins are always yellow. The splendidly coloured juveniles have a dark band over the head and a few vertical pale-blue lines on the body that are slightly curved.

Length to 45 cm.

Remarks: in the northern part of its range, the Queen angelfish is sympatric with the very similar *Holacanthus bermudensis*. These frequently hybridise and their offspring show all kinds of colour combinations. Apart from these hybrids, *H. ciliaris* produces some amazing colour morphs in St. Paul's Rocks, an isolated area right on the equator off the coast of Brazil. These strange colour morphs are thought to be caused by inbreeding due to its isolation and small region size (see page 70).

Aquarium: this species often suffers from transportation stress, especially at a large size. Juveniles travel much better and are usually more likely to adapt to captivity and once established this species is easy to keep. It is not advisable to put it together with invertebrates, as normally *Holacanthus ciliaris* feeds primarily on sponges and corals. In the aquarium *H. ciliaris* usually stays small, rarely exceeding 25 cm, and may fail to get the full adult colour pattern, probably due to insufficiencies in the diet.

A

H. ciliaris. Cayman Island. Depth 10 m. Length 35 cm. Roger Steene.

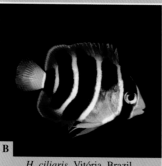

B

H. ciliaris. Vitória, Brazil.
Length 15 mm. João Gasparini.

C

H. ciliaris. St. Vincent, Caribbean.
D. 10 m. L. 45 mm. Roger Steene.

D

H. ciliaris. Bonaire, Netherlands Antilles.
Length 75 mm. Jan Post.

E

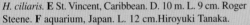

F

G

H. ciliaris. **E** St. Vincent, Caribbean. D. 10 m. L. 9 cm. Roger Steene. **F** aquarium, Japan. L. 12 cm.Hiroyuki Tanaka.

H. ciliaris. Adult. Laje de Santos I., Brazil. Osmar Luiz-Júnior.

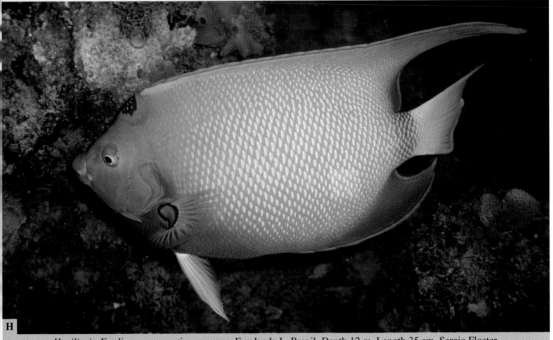

H

H. ciliaris. Feeding on encrusting sponges. Escalvada I., Brazil. Depth 12 m. Length 35 cm. Sergio Floeter.

Many divers dream of finding treasure, which is usually imagined as a sunken ship, chest filled with gold coins, or a submerged lost city of an ancient civilisation. The Saint Paul's Rocks, like a rocky "✕" in the middle of the Atlantic Ocean, is a perfect place for a hidden treasure. This very small group of rocky islands, situated just north of the equator (00°55'N, 29°21'W), has emerged on the Mid-Atlantic Ridge due to an upward thrust of the oceanic upper mantle. Being isolated by kilometres of oceanic deep water, this location has developed its own unique and exotic fauna with a high percentage of poorly known endemic reef fishes, as well as some wide-ranging species exhibiting abnormal behaviour compared to elsewhere. Beside these peculiarities, the most striking feature of Saint Paul's Rocks is a special population of queen angelfishes *Holacanthus ciliaris,* a common species here. Due to the separation and isolation from their mainland-coast counterparts, this population is susceptible to inbreeding and produces a small number of individuals featuring quite bizarre and sometimes beautiful colourations. Like rare precious stones, these are the swimming jewels, not found anywhere else in the world, except for the shallow waters around these rocky islands, an area covering about half a square kilometre.

The first to comment on these unusual colour morphs of the queen angelfish of St. Paul's Rocks were Lubbock and Edwards (1981) in their checklist of the reef fishes of the Rocks. Unfortunately, this paper provided no pictures. With the chance of photographing the unusually coloured queen angelfishes, I joined an expedition to the St. Paul's Rocks for a documentary as a photographer in 1999, and the results are presented here.

Besides the 'koi'- and a golden-coloured morph, other colour morphs were photographed and the images of the various forms were presented for the first time in scientific and technical publications (Joyeux et al. 2001; Luiz-Júnior 2003; Feitoza et al. in press). White and blue coloured morphs appear to be the more common varieties after the golden morph. The occurrence of morphs with mixed colours between the more common varieties, eg. blue body with yellow face or blue body with golden fins, seems to indicate that the colour development can be randomly placed in an individual, and so new combinations may be expected in the future.

It is really a marvellous experience to dive and photograph around the Rocks. The extremely clear water conditions allowed us to take good images as deep as 50 metres. Many inhabitants are uncommon and rarely found species

H. ciliaris. Golden morph of St. Paul's Rocks. Osmar Luiz-Júnior.

on the Brazilian continental coast, like the trumpetfish *Aulostomus strigosus*, black durgon (triggerfish) *Melichtys niger*, and scrawled filefish *Aluterus scriptus*, whilst the queen angelfish *Holacanthus ciliaris* was much more common here than on the coastal reefs of Brazil. Numerous moray eels were moving about on the bottom, and often seeing two or more individuals in the same hole led us to think that there were more eels than holes available. Endemic species that we only knew from scientific papers with black and white illustrations swam in living colours in front of us. It was all too easy to use up an entire 36 exposure roll of film in less than fifteen minutes of diving.

Literature cited

Feitoza, B.M., Rocha, L.A., Luiz-Júnior, O.J., Floeter, S.R. & Gasparini, J.L. *In press*. Reef fishes of St. Paul's Rocks: new records and notes on biology and zoogeography. *Aqua, Journal of ichthyology and Aquatic Biology*.

Joyeux, J.C., Floeter, S.R., Ferreira, C.E.L., & Gasparini, J.L., 2001. Biogeography of tropical reef fishes: the south Atlantic puzzle. *Journal of Biogeography* 28: 831-841.

Lubbock, R. & Edwards, A., 1981. The fishes of Saint Paul's Rocks. *Journal of Fish Biology* 18: 135-157.

Luiz-Júnior, O.J., 2003. Colour morphs in a queen angelfish *Holacanthus ciliaris* (Perciformes: Pomacanthidae) population of St. Paul's Rocks, NE Brazil. *Tropical Fish Hobbyist* 51(5): 82-90.

H. ciliaris. A white, 'koi' and a blue morph. Osmar Luiz-Júnior.

H. ciliaris. A ghostly white morph, showing no colour pigmentation at all. Lola Fritzsche.

Recent publication of these rare and beautifully coloured morphs has created a high demand in the ornamental fish trade and some of these morphs have already been collected. However, the removal of adult specimens could seriously effect this population. Understandably the desire to have such rare fishes is great and ideally someone could start an aquaculture of *Holacanthus ciliaris*, as already has been done with several angelfish genera in the Pacific. Someone could develop the skill by using specimens from coastal Brazilian waters, and when ready, collecting a few specimens from St. Paul's Rocks to produce different colour morphs. The technique used in *Pomacanthus arcuatus* and *P. paru*, collecting and mixing the gametes, would probably apply to this species, but developing food for raising the offspring may be more demanding.

A breeding stock should commence with normally coloured individuals for several reasons:

- we do not know what the effect will be on the population if morphs are removed.
- there is no doubt that their offspring would have the potential for different morphs anyway.

A number of morph specimens were shipped to Japan, fetching very high prices. Unfortunately for the buyer, after being kept for a period of time, they changed to the normal colouration of the typical Queen Angelfish. Perhaps the situation is the same as in the coral sea with some of the *Centropyge* spp (see pp 177 & 187).

H. ciliaris. A patchy blue-orange morph. **B** Lola Fritzsche. **C** similar morph, taken 20 years earlier. Roger Lubbock.

H. ciliaris. Golden morph of St. Paul's Rocks. Osmar Luiz-Júnior.

H. ciliaris. A blue morph with bright yellow pectoral and caudal fins, against a typical rocky back-drop. Lola Fritzsche.

Blue Angelfish *Holacanthus bermudensis*

Holacanthus ciliaris bermudensis Goode 1876. No locality.

Limited distribution in the western Atlantic, ranging from Bermuda westward to Florida into the Gulf of Mexico, and becoming rare in the southern Caribbean Sea. Occurs in shallow lagoons as well as deep coral reefs to a depth of about 90 m, and is usually seen solitary or in pairs. Adults of this species have an overall bluish grey colouration and the tips of the dorsal and anal fins, tail and pectoral fins are bordered with yellow. Juveniles closely resemble juvenile *Holacanthus ciliaris,* but the blue vertical stripes are straight, not curved like in the blue angelfish *H. bermudensis.* In general, this species is less colourful than *H. ciliaris.* Its crown on the forehead is just a hint of the typical '*ciliaris*-crown". Length to 45 cm.

Remarks: Holacanthus ciliaris and *H. bermudensis* frequently hybridise. These natural hybrids were described as the species *Angelichthys townsendi* Nicholds & Mowbray 1914, and even today the morphs are sometimes traded as the species *Holacanthus townsendi.* As a described hybrid species it should be expressed as *Holacanthus ✕ townsendi.*

Aquarium: adapts poorly to captivity, and, like *Holacanthus ciliaris,* is delicate and sensitive to handling, often suffering transportation stress. Chances for success are best when introducing them as juveniles and offering a variety of food and optimum water quality conditions.

A *H. bermudensis.* Aquarium. Length 4 cm. Alex Kerstich.

B *H. bermudensis.* Aquarium. Length 7 cm. Rudie Kuiter.

C *H. bermudensis.* Florida Keys. Depth 10 m. Length 35 cm. Roger Steene.

D

H. bermudensis. Florida. Large adult with cleaner goby. Lawson Wood.

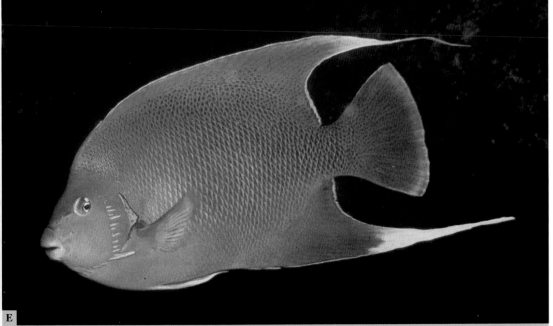

E

Holacanthus **X***townsendi.* Bermuda. The population in this region are thought to comprise mainly hybrids. Luiz Rocha.

GENUS *Holacanthus*, SUBGENUS *Plitops* Burton, 1934

Masculine. Type species: *Holacanthus clarionensis* Gilbert, 1890. The subgenus *Plitops* comprises 3 eastern Pacific species. Each species with distinctive colouration and easily identified at all stages.

Species Picture Index to adults and juveniles

| *H. passer* 78 | *H. clarionensis* 80 | *H. limbaughi* 82 |

Holacanthus passer. Working as cleaner, inspecting Hammerhead Sharks. Galapagos Islands. Peter Kragh.

Holacanthus passer. Massing adults, mixing with *Prionurus laticlavius.* Galápagos Islands. Doug Perrine.

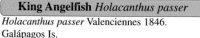

Holacanthus passer Valenciennes 1846.
Galápagos Is.

Tropical eastern Pacific, from the Galápagos Islands northeast via Panama and Costa Rica to the Gulf of California (Sea of Cortez), Mexico. Occurs on shallow algae-covered rocky reefs to about 80 m depth. It can tolerate water temperatures as low as only 12 to 22°C, surviving the cold Humboldt current reaching from the south into the tropical eastern Pacific. The King angelfish is often shy and usually solitary, but in some areas it is easily approached and sometimes encountered in large aggregations. Readily identified by its beautiful colours. Males clearly grow larger and bulkier than females and whilst females have yellow ventral fins, males have white ones. Juveniles have vertical blue lines on their rear half, the first one giving rise to the white bar. Length to 25 cm.

Remarks: apart from very similar colouration of the juveniles, the crown on the forehead of *Holacanthus passer* is like that of the Atlantic *H. ciliaris*. The Queen and the King angelfish obviously share a common ancestor. When the author was diving in the Gulf of California, Mexico in 1976, he was stunned when 30 or so King angelfishes came straight up to him. To watch such an aggregation was overwhelming! Juvenile King angelfishes commonly clean ectoparasites from other fishes. Adults also clean and this has been reported many times from the Sea of Cortez, Mexico, and at Cocos Island, Costa Rica, even patiently waiting for hammerhead sharks!

Aquarium: imports of *Holacanthus passer* to Germany began in the early 1970's when little information about this species was available. A 13 cm long King angelfish was easily kept, but very aggressive towards inmates.

A

H. passer. Large juvenile, its blue vertical lines beginning to break up. Length ~12 cm. Galápagos. Graham Edgar.

B

H. passer. Cocos I., Costa Rica. Length 7 cm. Cleaning Creolefish *Paranthias*, which assists in paling its colour to show-up parasites. Peter Kragh.

C

D

H. passer. **C** Cocos I., Costa Rica. Length 7 cm. Peter Kragh. **D** Sea of Cortez. Length 4 cm. Roger Steene.

D

H. passer. Sea of Cortez. Depth 12 m. Length 20 cm. Helmut Debelius.

E

H. passer. Large adult. Galápagos Graham Edgar.

Clarion Angelfish *Holacanthus clarionensis*

Holacanthus clarionensis Gilbert 1891. Clarion, Sorocco and San Benedicto Is., Revilla Gigedo Is., off w. Mexico.

Eastern Pacific, ranging from off Mexico, Revillagigedo Islands, north to the southern part of the Gulf of California and south to Clipperton Island. Inhabits shallow rocky and coastal reefs to a depth of about 30 m. Small juveniles are solitary, whilst adults are often single or in small groups, but also form large schools in some localities. Adults of this splendid fish are brilliant orange, their breast and caudal fin being the brightest. The dorsal and anal fins have an irridescent blue margin. Males grow bigger than females, looking somewhat more rounded, and have a darker head. Juveniles have blue vertical lines on the head and posterior part of the body that darken with age and eventually fade away. Length to 23 cm.

H. clarionensis. Aquarium. Length 20 cm. Rudie Kuiter.

H. clarionensis. Clarion I. large juvenile. Jerry Allen.

H. clarionensis. Schooling adults when feeding are a truly spectacular sight. Their bright orange and yellow colours are a sharp contrast to the otherwise drab natural environment in which they live. Revilla Gigedo Island. Jerry Allen.

Remarks: adult *Holacanthus clarionensis* are often seen cleaning big elasmobranchs, such as silvertip sharks and manta rays. The temptation for a special meal must be enough to move from the safer rocky reefs into open water to serve waiting customers, often high above the substrate. Named after Clarion Island.

Aquarium: a long-lived and easily kept, but aggressive species. It is important that water temperatures are not too high. The Clarion Angelfish is regularly traded into Europe, Japan and North America, but very expensive due to the high cost of collecting and transporting from remote areas. In public aquariums this species is kept in groups, but only in the large spacious displays where they can stay out of harm's way or make friends.

E
H. clarionensis. Clarion I. L. 45 mm. Ross Robertson.

F
H. clarionensis. Not particularly worried by the photographer. Large male in front. Revilla Gigedo I. Michelle Hall.

G
H. clarionensis. Schooling adults on the move, probably to another feeding site. Swimming closely together may give the impression of being a single large body and avoid attack from predators. Revilla Gigedo Island. Jerry Allen.

H. limbaughi. Aquarium, Hawaii. Helmut Debelius.

Clipperton Angelfish *Holacanthus limbaughi*
Holacanthus limbaughi Baldwin 1963.
Nw. shore of Clipperton I., east Pacific.

Endemic to Clipperton Island in the Eastern Pacific. Occurs on near-shore reefs at depths to about 40 m, but mainly common in the shallow coral-rich habitats. Adults solitary, in pairs or small groups, whilst juveniles mainly solitary. Adults are mostly bluish grey with a darker head, a large white tail and ventral fins white with blue margin. The dorsal and anal fins are angled and have brilliant blue margins, and there is a distinctive white spot on the upper side of the body, just below the lateral-line. Juveniles have narrow blue vertical lines on head and body. Length to 24 cm.

Remarks: the first specimens were caught in 1958 and preserved in alcohol in which their colour was lost. Live colouration was uncertain until 1994, when ichthyologist Gerald Allen photographed this species during an expedition to the area and his photographs are presented here. Clipperton Island is the only true coral atoll in the eastern Pacific and is situated over 1000 km from the Mexican coast at a latitude of 10°N. This tiny, lonely spot in the biggest ocean covers an area of less than 10 square kilometres, and it comprises a freshwater lake encircled by a narrow strip of land. The reef slopes are covered richly with stony-coral formations.

Aquarium: one of the rarest angelfish in the aquarium trade. In 2001 the author photographed a Clipperton angelfish in the Waikiki Aquarium, Hawaii. It was kept by the director, Bruce Carlson, in his office, taking care of this special fish personally! His specimen was collected on a private expedition to Clipperton a year earlier and according to Bruce it adapted quickly to captivity, in a matter of weeks accepting any substitute food offered.

H. limbaughi. Juvenile. Clipperton I. Jerry Allen.

H. limbaughi. Subadult. Clipperton I. Jerry Allen.

H. limbaughi. Large adult, about 24 cm long. Clipperton I. Jerry Allen.

H. limbaughi. Congregating adults. Clipperton I. Jerry Allen.

Masculine. Type species: *Holacanthus xanthurus* Bleeker 1853. The genus *Apolemichthys* currently comprises 8 species, sometimes called Smoke Angelfishes. They are medium sized pomacanthids with the species ranging in body length from about 15 to 25 cm. All occur in various parts of the Indo-Pacific Ocean. These angelfishes are similar to the genus *Holacanthus,* which are mainly found in the Atlantic Ocean, but differ in the finer features, eg. their preorbital convex is without strong spines. Some species of this genus are endemic to a certain region, eg. *Apolemichthys arcuatus* is known only from the Hawaiian island chain and *Apolemichthys guezei* only from Réunion, an island in the Southern Indian Ocean. Almost all smoke angelfishes occur below 15 m, and are only rarely encountered in shallow water with *A. xanthotis* being an exception in the Red Sea. Their occurrence or appearance is never abundant, rather scarce, and sporadic. Outer reefs with rich coral growth and sponges are the preferred habitat where most species live either singly or in pairs. Contrary to various other angelfish genera, adult *Apolemichthys*-species display no sexual differences. Only the juvenile patterns are different from those of the adult and in some species even this is rather minor. All species of *Apolemichthys* are thought to be food specialists, feeding primarily on sponges. Maintaining them in aquaria is thus never accomplished without problems. Exceptions are the tough and very similar species *A. xanthurus* and *A. xanthotis* from the northern and central Indian Ocean around the Arabian Peninsula respectively. In a modern reef aquarium many individuals may feed on the corals, which can be harmed by this. By far the most collected species of the Smoke-angelfish genus for the aquarium trade is the Three-spot Angelfish *Apolemichthys trimaculatus*. This species is widespread and co-occurs with other members of the genus and may hybridise with them. Such a hybrid morph was described as *Apolemichthys armitagei* Smith 1955. A rare form to be found around the Indian Ocean islands of the Seychelles and the Maldives, and thus is now treated as a described hybrid: *A.* X *armitagei*. Dennis King recently photographed a hybrid of *A. kingi* (his name-sake) and *A. trimaculatus* at the Aliwal Shoal, just south of Durban, South Africa.

1	*A. arcuatus*	*Holacanthus arcuatus* Gray, 1831. Hawaiian Is.	(p. 98)
2	*A. griffisi*	*Holacanthus griffisi* Carlson & Taylor, 1981. Canton & n. Phoenix Is., s. Pacific.	(p. 96)
3	*A. guezei*	*Holacanthus guezei* Randall & Mauge, 1978. Réunion I.	(p. 96)
4	*A. kingi*	*Apolemichthys kingi* Heemstra, 1984. Off Durban, South Africa.	(p. 92)
5	*A. trimaculatus*	*Holacanthus trimaculatus* Cuvier, 1831. Moluccas.	(p. 88)
6	*A. xanthopunctatus*	*Apolemichthys xanthopunctatus* Burgess, 1973. Fanning & Line Islands, c. Pacific.	(p. 94)
7	*A. xanthotis*	*Holacanthus xanthotis* Fraser-Brunner, 1951. Mukalla Bay, South Arabia.	(p. 87)
8	*A. xanthurus*	*Holacanthus xanthurus* Bennett, 1833. Sri Lanka.	(p. 86)

The named hybrid *Apolemichthys* X *armitagei* photographed in the Maldives. Its parent species *A. trimaculatus* and *A. xanthurus* are commonly seen there, both occurring in the same invertebrate-rich and sponge-dominated habitats. Rudie Kuiter.

A. xanthurus **86**	A. xanthotis **87**	A. xanthotis **87**
A. trimaculatus **88**	A. trimaculatus **88**	A. Xarmitagei **91**
A. kingi X trimaculatus **91**	A. kingi **92**	A. kingi **92**
A. xanthopunctatus **94**	A. xanthopunctatus **94**	A. guezei **96**

A. griffisi **96**

A. griffisi **96**   A. arcuatus **98**

A. *xanthurus*. Mauritius. Length about 14 cm. Hugues Vitry.

Indian Smoke-angelfish *Apolemichthys xanthurus*

Holacanthus xanthurus Bennett, 1833. Sri Lanka.

Indian Ocean, Mauritius to the Maldives, Sri Lanka and India. In the Maldives in coral-rich outer reef habitats with lots of hiding places at depths to ~45 m, whilst in Sri Lanka on coastal reefs in murky water from rivers. Coloured white to yellow-grey and scales on mid and upper sides have a small black centre-spot that increases in size dorsally. Head is dark to the posterior edge of the operculum, and the caudal fin is brilliantly yellow. Length to 15 cm.

Remarks: the Indian Smoke-angelfish is shy, quickly diving for cover when disturbed. It is very similar to *Apolemichthys xanthotis* and the two species are frequently confused. Both species have similar colour patterns. In *A. xanthurus* the dark head colouration is posteriorly restricted to the operculum edge and in *A xanthotis* to the axil. It may hybridise with *A. trimaculatus* (see p. 91).

Aquarium: the Indian smoke-angelfish is quickly acclimatised, docile, and easy to maintain. Perhaps not one of the most beautiful angelfishes, but highly recommended.

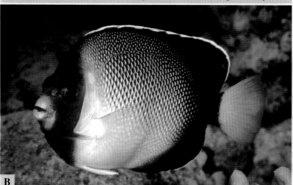

B
A. *xanthurus*. Maldives. D. 35 m. L. 15 cm. Rudie Kuiter.

C
A. *xanthurus*. Aquarium. Juvenile. Hiroyuki Tanaka.

D
A. *xanthurus*. Maldives. Depth 30 m. Length 12 cm. Rudie Kuiter.

Arabian Smoke-angelfish
Apolemichthys xanthotis

Holacanthus xanthotis Fraser-Brunner, 1951.
South Arabia.

Known from around the Arabian Peninsula, from the Gulf of Aqaba in the Red Sea to Kuwait in the Arabian Gulf, and Kenya. Usually found at the coral-rich fringing reefs of the Red Sea at 5–80 m and more shallow at the rocky coast of Oman and inside the sandy Arabian Gulf. Adults are identified by their dark head, a pale body that is almost surrounded by a black band going from over the dorsal to anal fins, running over caudal peduncle, and its yellow caudal fin. The pale-blue border on the dorsal and anal fins, and a yellow to orange 'ear' spot on the dusky background are other distinctive features. Juveniles have a broad black eye-band and most of the posterior part of the body is black, features that gradually change with age. Length to 15 cm.

A

A. xanthotis. Aqaba, Jordan. D. 7 m. L. 15 cm. Helmut Debelius.

B

A. xanthotis. Oman. L. 35 mm. John Hoover.

Remarks: during "El Niño" in 1998 currents carried pelagic stages to the African coast and *Apolemichthys xanthotis* was recorded on the coast of Kenya for the first time, and was quite common then. It was confirmed that these expatriates were not the similar *Apolemichthys xanthurus* that is found in the adjacent western Indian Ocean. On the east coast of the Gulf of Aqaba, Red Sea (Jordan and Saudi-Arabia) *A. xanthotis* occurs in small groups in very shallow water, but on the west coast (Sinai Peninsula) the author observed only a single individual at a depth of 80 m when conducting a test dive on the Ras Mohammed drop-off.

Aquarium: the Arabian Smoke-angelfish is reputed as being easy to keep, but is much rarer in the trade than its relative *Apolemichthys xanthurus* from the Indian Ocean.

C

A. xanthotis. Muscat, Oman. Depth 18 m. Length 15 cm. Helmut Debelius.

A. trimaculatus. Seychelles. D. 25 m. L. 24 cm. Helmut Debelius.

A. trimaculatus. Aliwal Shoal, South Africa. L. 12 cm. Rudie Kuiter.

Three-spot Angelfish *Apolemichthys trimaculatus*
Holacanthus trimaculatus Cuvier, 1831. Moluccas.

Indo-Pacific, ranging from East Africa and the Maldives to Samoa, South Pacific, north as far as Japan and south to New Caledonia, but Indian Ocean and Pacific forms are different. Most notable is the blue under the eye of the Pacific form that is absent in the Indian Ocean form. Found in clear lagoons and outer reefs at depths of 3–60 m, but prefers mainly deeper zones of the reef. Depending on the area, the Three-spot Angelfish swims solitary, in pairs or occasionally in small groups. Small groups are thought to represent harems in Indonesia and Micronesia, Central Pacific. The most common and widespread Smoke-angelfish species. This fish shines beautifully yellow, and has three name-giving spots: a black one (often split in two in adults) on the forehead, and one on each side (almost the colour of the body), 'ear-like', behind the head. Other distinct features are the brilliantly blue lips, and the caudal fin divided into white and black. Juveniles show a distinct black blotch at the posterior upper base of the dorsal fin and dark eye stripe. Length to 25 cm.

Remarks: this species hybridises in the Maldives and Seychelles with *Apolemichthys xanthurus,* producing a known form that was described as *Apolemichthys armitagei,* and is occasionally traded as such in the aquarium industry.

Aquarium: reputed as being delicate and susceptible to carrying parasites. In the wild, *Apolemichthys trimaculatus* mainly feeds on sponges and sea squirts, many individuals, however, readily accept food substitutes. Maintaining them in coral reef aquaria is not advisable. The 'delicate' species may get quite aggressive towards very similarly coloured inmates. Its stays smaller in the aquarium than in the wild, usually less than 20 cm long, and has spawned in captivity. Can live for as long as 24 years.

A. trimaculatus. Large adult. Typical Pacific form with blue eye shade. Kerama, Japan. Rudie Kuiter.

A. trimaculatus. Yellow-spotted variation with *Labroides* cleaner. Flores, Indonesia. Depth 20 m. Length 15 cm. Rudie Kuiter.

A. trimaculatus. Large adult. Typical Indian Ocean form with no eye shade. Maldives. Rudie Kuiter.

A. trimaculatus. Bali, Indonesia. Depth 25 m. Length 9 cm. Rudie Kuiter.

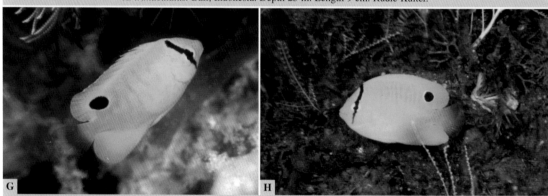

A. trimaculatus. Mabul, Malaysia. D. 35 m. L. 6 cm. Derawan, Indonesia. D. 35 m. L. 5 cm. Rudie Kuiter.

A. trimaculatus. Bali, Indonesia. Depth 25 m. Length ~20 cm. Rudie Kuiter.

Few species of *Apolemichthys* co-occur. Only the range of the widespread *A. trimaculatus* is such that it encompasses other congeners. Usually the adults of each species form small groups of their own, in a harem fashion in which a single male dominates several females in a territory established by the male. Post-larval juveniles may settle in a given territory and join such a harem when they mature. When closely related territorial species co-occur, they usually compete and defend their own section from invaders including males of their own and related species. However settling juveniles are not recognised as a threat and if two different species are common in a particular region, the chances of a juvenile of another species becoming part of the harem of the 'wrong' species is rather high. This seems to be the case in some parts of the Maldives where both *A. trimaculatus* and *A. xanthurus* are moderately common. Here, the hybrid of these parent species *A. X armitagei* is a regular occurrence. This morph usually shows a resemblance to both parents, but individuals are variable, especially in the amount of black pigmentation on the dorsal fin. Another hybrid that has recently become known is that of *A. kingi* and *A. trimaculatus* as the parent species. There are several more species that co-occur with *A. trimaculatus* and additional hybrids may be expected.

Hybrid Smoke-angelfish
Apolemichthys X armitagei
Apolemichthys armitagei Smith, 1955. Seychelles.

A hybrid morph known from the Maldives and Seychelles regions of the parent species *Apolemichthys trimaculatus* and *A. xanthurus*. It is moderately common in some parts of the Maldives and usually seen at depths of about 20–30 m. Although it appears to live solitary, it may be pairing or be part of a small group comprising itself, and one of the parent species. Finding a number of hybrid individuals together would be very rare. The hybrid form is identified by its yellowish colour, derived from *A. trimaculatus,* and the dusky head and black blotch on the soft-rayed part of the dorsal fin. Length 20–22 cm.

A. Xarmitagei. Maldives. Length 20 cm. Depth 24 m. Rudie Kuiter.

Hybrid Tiger Angelfish
Apolemichthys kingi X trimaculatus
Undescribed hybrid.

This beautifully yellow hybrid tiger-angelfish is here reported for the first time. Of the parent species, *Apolemichthys kingi* and *A. trimaculatus,* the former by far outnumbers the latter at the photo-locality: the Aliwal Shoal of the coast of South Africa, just south of Durban. In this area, small groups of *A. kingi* are moderately common at about 30 m depth, whilst the occasional solitary *A. trimaculatus* is seen in the same general areas. This morph appears to be extremely rare. It will probably reach 24 cm in length as both parent species reach this size at the same locality.

A. kingi X trimaculatus. Aliwal Shoal. D. 30 m. L. 16 cm. Dennis King.

Tiger Angelfish
Apolemichthys kingi

Apolemichthys kingi Heemstra, 1984.
Off Durban, South Africa.

Appears to be restricted to subtropical waters from just south of Bazaruto in Mozambique to East London in SA. The Tiger Angelfish is moderately common on rocky offshore reefs (Aliwal Shoal) at 20–50 m depth, but usually seen deeper than 25 m where sponges are more common. Often occurs in small loose groups. A timid species which withdraws to deep crevices or swims away when approached. With no other similar species in its range, this species is readily identified. Top half of the body is black with wavy yellow lines, grading to a uniformly pale grey ventrally, head and breast are sooty dark. There is a black spot behind the head. Dorsal and caudal fins have a narrow light border. Juveniles with fewer 'tiger-stripes' and a yellow-edged black ocellus at base of soft dorsal fin. Length to 24 cm.

Remarks: this species feeds primarily on sponges and other inverts. It was named after the South African UW-photographer Dennis King, who discovered and then collected it together with the late Peter van Niekerk.

Aquarium: one individual was imported into Germany recently and became a docile member of a fish community tank, and one other into Japan that is doing well.

A. kingi. Aliwal Shoal, off South Africa. D. 35 m. L. 18 cm. Dennis King.

A. kingi. Aliwal Shoal, off eastern coast of South Africa. Depth 28 m. Length 24 cm. Rudie Kuiter.

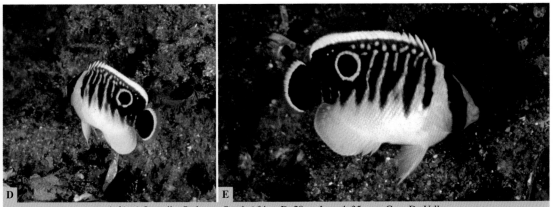

A. kingi. Juvenile. Sodwana South Africa. D. 28 m. Length 35 mm. Greg De Valle.

A. kingi. Aliwal Shoal, South Africa. Depth 28 m. Length 22 cm. Rudie Kuiter.

A. kingi. Aliwal Shoal, off eastern coast of South Africa. Depth 25 m. Length 24 cm. Dennis King.

A

A. xanthopunctatus. Marshall Is. Length ~14 cm. Marshall Yoshii.

B

A. xanthopunctatus. Aquarium. Length 20 cm. Helmut Debelius.

Apolemichthys xanthopunctatus Burgess, 1973.
Fanning & Line Islands, Central Pacific.

Pacific regions from the northern Cook Islands west to Kiribati and Micronesia. Found near coral reefs in lagoons and in gutters on outer reefs at depths between 3 and 50 m. Occurs usually solitary, in pairs or occasionally in small groups. This very attractive species has three blotches and a blue mouth region like *Apolemichthys trimaculatus*. The broad black rims of the fins are reminiscent of *A. xanthotis,* and are beautifully margined with irridescent blue in *A. xanthopunctatus*. A black blotch on the forehead is also distinct, as is the very long blue cheek spine. Length to 25 cm.

Remarks: the name *xanthopunctatus* is in reference to the numerous golden spots on the body flanks. Juveniles of the Golden-spotted Angelfish feature a big white-edged black ocellus at the rear of the body and on the soft part of the dorsal fin.

Aquarium: the author saw this species in the 1980s in a display tank at the Frankfurt Senckenberg Museum and watched it for many years. Seemingly the most beautiful species of its genus, it was the attraction for many marine aquarists in the area, since the species was only rarely imported to Germany then. According to its keeper, Horst Zetzsche, this species was very docile, and accepted any food offered by him, preferring live or fresh mussel meat.

C

A. xanthopunctatus. Cook Islands, south Pacific. Depth 18 m. Length 20 cm. Helmut Debelius.

A. xanthopunctatus. Juvenile stages in aquarium. **D** Hiroyuki Tanaka. **E** Richard Pyle.

A. xanthopunctatus. Cook Islands, south Pacific. Depth 18 m. Length 20 cm. Helmut Debelius.

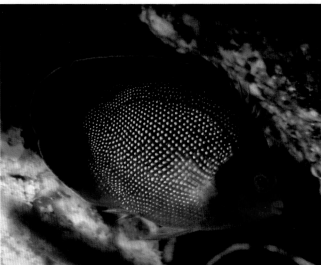

Holacanthus guezei Randall & Mauge, 1978. Réunion I.

Only known from specimens and a few photographs. Habitat of *Apolemichthys guezei* appears to be deep outer-reefs at Réunion. The types were collected using gill nets at the French island Réunion in the southwestern Indian Ocean. Specifically off Baie de la Possession on the west coast at 60–80 m, in 1973 and 1974. Hugues Vitry, a Mauritius dive master keenly interested in ichthyology made several trips to his neighbouring island to find and collect this species on the deep reefs there. Eventually he found one on the way up from a deep dive and, whilst rushed for time, he managed to get just one, but perfect shot. This species is similar to *A. xanthopunctatus* in having lots of small yellow spots, but it lacks the black nape and 'ear' spot. Its dark appearance underwater is perhaps why it has gone unnoticed for so long. Length to 15 cm.

Remarks: named after Paul Guézé, its discoverer and collector of the specimens.

A. guezei. Réunion. Depth 65 m Length 10 cm. Hugues Vitry.

Griffis' Angelfish *Apolemichthys griffisi*

Holacanthus griffisi Carlson & Taylor, 1981.
Canton & n. Phoenix Is., South Pacific.

Known from central Pacific islands such as the Marshall and Line Islands (Kiribati) westward to the Solomon Islands, Papua New Guinea and Indonesia. This species occurs mainly on deep outer-reef walls at depths over 40 m (10–60 m). Not often seen, usually solitary. Identified by the generally grey colour and a distinct white stripe along the base of the dorsal fin that continues into the caudal-fin base, making a real contrast to the black back. Length to 25 cm.

Aquarium: one pair of Griffis' angelfish was kept in Hawaii's Waikiki Aquarium for a long time and was provided with a varied diet. According to its director Bruce Carlson (and author of *Apolemichthys griffisi*) the Griffis' Angelfish is docile like the other *Apolemichthys* members.

A

A. griffisi. Aquarium. Length 22 cm. Rudie Kuiter.

B   C

A. griffisi. **B** Aquarium. Adult. Helmut Debelius. **C** Aquarium. Juvenile. Christmas I, (Kiritimati). L. ~8 cm. Richard Pyle.

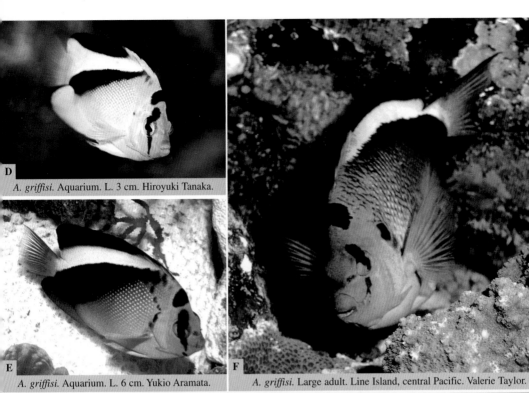

D *A. griffisi.* Aquarium. L. 3 cm. Hiroyuki Tanaka.

E *A. griffisi.* Aquarium. L. 6 cm. Yukio Aramata.

F *A. griffisi.* Large adult. Line Island, central Pacific. Valerie Taylor.

G *A. griffisi.* Marshall Islands. Juvenile. Marshall Yoshii.

97

A

A. arcuatus. Adult. Hawaiian Islands. Ed Robinson.

Bandit Angelfish *Apolemichthys arcuatus*

Holacanthus arcuatus Gray, 1831. Hawaiian Islands.

Known only from the Hawaiian Islands, west to Midway Atoll and south to Johnston Island in the central Pacific Ocean. Preferred habitats are outer rocky reefs and caves at depths between 20 and 70 m, but also observed from submersibles way below 100 m. Seen singly and in pairs. A distinctly coloured species, characterised by a broad dark longitudinal stripe. The lighter edged black-brown band crosses over the eye and extends to the end of the dorsal fin, practically dividing the body into a white and a light brown zone. Anal and caudal fins also have a white-edged dark band. Juveniles are very similarly patterned, but the black body stripe reaches the dorsal fin and extends around the mouth. Length to 18 cm.

Remarks: Some scientists placed this species into Fowler's (1941) monotypic genus *Desmoholacanthus*, but this name was shown to be invalid in a paper on phylogenetic relationships published by the Chinese University of Hong Kong (K. Chung and N. Woo, 1998).

Aquarium: artificial hiding places are readily accepted. Generally this species is described as very delicate due almost certainly to its natural food source - it feeds primarily on sponges. Keeping this species in a living reef aquarium is not recommended as the bandit angelfish will feed on other sessile invertebrates as well. It is possible to place several individuals together without the problems that are often encountered with other angelfishes, due to their docile nature. Diving with fish collectors around Big Island Hawaii, the author learned that *Apolemichthys arcuatus* are easily collected with hand nets.

B

A. arcuatus. Tiny juvenile. Yukio Aramata.

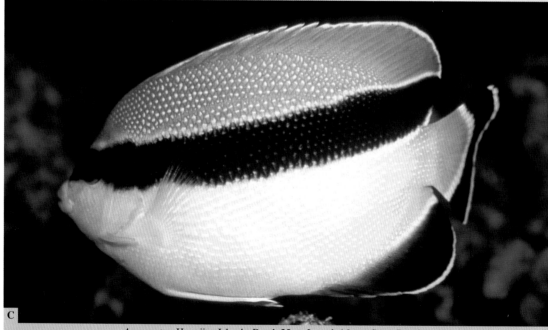

C

A. arcuatus. Hawaiian Islands. Depth 25 m. Length 16 cm. Steve Drogin.

D

A. arcuatus. Aquarium. With cleaner shrimp *Lysmata amboinensis* checking the gills. Helmut Debelius.

E

A. arcuatus. Hawaiian Islands. Depth 42 m. Length 15 cm. Helmut Debelius.

GENUS *Chaetodontoplus* Bleeker, 1876

Masculine. Type species: *Holacanthus (Chaetodontoplus) septentrionalis* Temminck & Schlegel, 1844. Comprises about 14 species, but species complexes are poorly understood and several species may be reclassified according to preliminary research. The members are restricted to the western edge of the Pacific, mainly tropical coastal waters of Southeast Asia, Papua New Guinea and Australia. Most species have a very limited range, or live at depth and are rarely encountered in their natural habitat. As a group they are known as Velvet Angelfishes due to the colour of some species and due to them having the smallest scales in the angelfish family, giving a number of species a 'velvet' look. The *Chaetodontoplus* members are medium-sized angelfishes, averaging about 20 cm, which feed mainly on sponges and tunicates. Most species live on invertebrate-rich reefs, singly, in pairs, and some species may form small groups for safety when feeding, or in some a male dominates a small number of females in a claimed territory. There is no very obvious sexual dimorphism in most species, and usually this consists of additional colouration or marking, e.g *Chaetodontoplus duboulayi* males have a prominent white patch behind the eye, but in a number of species the male elongates in its overall shape compared to the female and usually gets larger. Unlike most other angelfishes, some species in this genus are rather drab, but on the other hand, there are several beauties as well, some of which are amongst the favourites of the advanced aquarist. These fishes often refuse to eat when placed in captivity, but this usually applies to adults adapted to a special diet. However, refusal to eat may also be the result of the collecting method or the way they are handled after collection. In the aquarium, they are often rather shy at first and plenty of hiding places should be provided using rocks, especially if the individuals are adults.

With regards to the classification, this genus appears to comprise a number of closely related species that are confusing even amongst specialists, especially for those working in the taxonomy field who have not observed the species in the wild. Some species are known from just a few specimens, whilst others have identical phases between different species at some stage of their life. Juveniles are often identical in every detail but grow into different adults. Apart from *C. mesoleucus*, none of the other *Chaetodontoplus* members are widespread. *C. melanosoma* was thought to have a relatively large geographical range, however it is now clear that this is incorrect and a case of mistaken identities.

The Japanese researchers Toshiaki Tominaga and Fujio Yasuda presented a paper at the Thirteenth Pacific Science Congress in 1975, summarising their preliminary work on their intended revision of the genus, in which they discussed the removal of the species *mesoleucus* and *niger* from the genus. This was mainly concluded after examining radiographs of different genera within Pomacanthidae showing that certain genera have a single predorsal bone and others have two. All the species of *Centropyge, Genicanthus, Holacanthus,* and *Pygoplites* have, without exception, a single bone, whilst *Pomacanthus* and most of *Chaetodontoplus* have two, but *niger* and *mesoleucus* placed in this genus have only one. These are important characteristics, but more research is required and if proven different, they need to be described and named as there is no other name available for either species. For now we suggest no changes.

List of species.

1.	*C. ballinae*	*Chaetodontoplus ballinae* Whitley, 1959. NSW, Australia. (p. **122**)
2.	*C. cephalareticulatus*	*Chaetodontoplus cephalareticulatus* Shen & Kim, 1975. Taiwan. (p. **106**)
3.	*C. chrysocephalus*	*Holacanthus chrysocephalus* Bleeker, 1854. Java. (p. **110**)
4.	*C. conspicillatus*	*Holacanthus conspicillatus* Waite, 1900. Lord Howe Island. (p. **126**)
5.	*C. dimidiatus*	*Chaetodontoplus dimidiatus* Bleeker, 1860. Ambon, Indonesia. (p. **116**)
6.	*C. duboulayi*	*Holacanthus duboulayi* Günther, 1867. nw coast of Australia. (p. **124**)
7.	*C. melanosoma*	*Holacanthus melanosoma* Bleeker, 1853. Solor I., Indonesia. (p. **112**)
8.	*C. cf melanosoma*	*undescribed* (p. **114**)
9.	*C. meredithi*	*Chaetodontoplus meredithi* Kuiter, 1990. Sydney Harbour, Australia. (p. **118**)
10.	*C. mesoleucus*	*Chaetodon mesoleucus* Bloch, 1787. No locality. (p. **130**)
11.	*C. cf mesoleucus*	*undescribed* (p. **132**)
12.	*C. niger*	*Chaetodontoplus niger* Chan, 1966. Macclesfield Bank, South China Seas. (p. **128**)
13.	*C. personifer*	*Chaetodontoplus personifer* McCulloch, 1914. Western Australia. (p. **121**)
14.	*C. septentrionalis*	*Holacanthus (C.) septentrionalis* Temminck & Schlegel, 1844. Japan. (p. **102**)

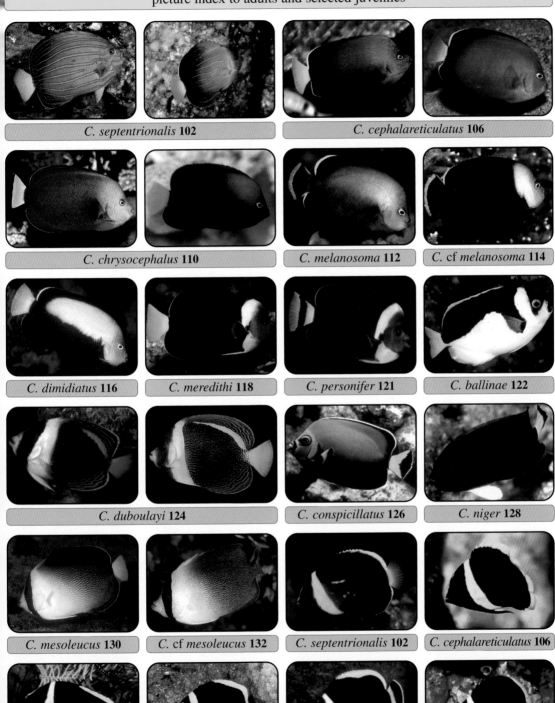

C. septentrionalis 102

C. cephalareticulatus 106

C. chrysocephalus 110

C. melanosoma 112

C. cf melanosoma 114

C. dimidiatus 116

C. meredithi 118

C. personifer 121

C. ballinae 122

C. duboulayi 124

C. conspicillatus 126

C. niger 128

C. mesoleucus 130

C. cf mesoleucus 132

C. septentrionalis 102

C. cephalareticulatus 106

C. melanosoma 112

C. cf melanosoma 114

C. dimidiatus 116

C. meredithi 118

Blue-striped Angelfish *Chaetodontoplus septentrionalis*

Holacanthus septentrionalis Temminck & Schlegel, 1844. Nagasaki, Japan.

Northern West-Pacific, Japan to Taiwan, and southern Korea to Hong Kong, but mainland populations look slightly different. Found on rocky coastal reefs at depths from about 5 to 60 m. It has electric blue stripes along its sides and a bright yellow tail. Post-larval juveniles are almost completely black, having a yellow band behind the eye that will disappear with growth. No sexual dichromatism is known and they occur in pairs or form a small harem, and females are only recognised when gravid by their swollen abdomen. It occurs together with a different colour form, similar to *Chaetodontoplus*

chrysocephalus, especially around Kashiwajima, western Shikoku and the Izu Peninsula, the sub-adults of which superficially resemble *C. melanosoma* and records of the latter are based on this form. It is not clear if this form is just a variation of *C. septentrionalis* or a separate species. Length to 22 cm.

Remarks: juveniles of different *Chaetodontoplus* species are often remarkably similar, with the tiny young being completely black with a yellowish band on neck. *C. septentrionalis* from southern Japan, *C. melanosoma,* cf *melanosoma* and *C. dimidiatus* in Indonesia and Papua New Guinea, and *C. meredithi* and *C. personifer* from Australia, seemingly forming a distinct group. The distribution of *Chaetodontoplus septentrionalis* (the commonest angelfish in southern Honshu, which is scarce in Ogasawara and absent from the Ryukyu Islands, while in Taiwan it is very common), seems to indicate a preference for mainland habitats and perhaps slightly cooler conditions. A unique variety from Vietnam has a complicated pattern of blue stripes or markings on its face. Shipments from Vietnam to Japan have become more regular and include this form on occasions, fetching a high price in Japan.

Aquarium: introduced large individuals usually refuse to eat, but juveniles take to some meaty foods or clams and will often feed on artificial flakes soon after. The general rule: juveniles adapt easier than adults, which applies to most large angelfish-species.

A

C. septentrionalis. Izu, Japan. Depth 20 m. Length 14 cm. Rudie Kuiter.

B

C. septentrionalis. Izu, Japan. Depth 30 m. Length 22 cm. Rudie Kuiter.

C *C. septentrionalis.* Probably male, judging by its elongated body. Izu, Japan. Depth 25 m. Length 20 cm. Rudie Kuiter.

D *C. septentrionalis.* Izu, Japan. Depth 40 m. Length 14 cm. Rudie Kuiter.

C. septentrionalis. Japan. **E** Osezaki. D. 15 m. L. 20 mm. Rudie Kuiter. **F** Osezaki. Depth 20 m. Length 7 cm. Roger Steene. **G** Izu. D. 35 m. L. 9 cm. **H** Izu. Depth 20 m. Length 12 cm. **I** Kashiwajima. Depth 22 m. Length 18 cm. Rudie Kuiter.

C. septentrionalis. Izu, Japan. Depth 30 m. Length 20 cm. Rudie Kuiter.

K

C. cf *septentrionalis.* Thick-striped variation. Hong Kong. Depth 18 m. Length 15 cm. Keith Wilson.

L

C. cf *septentrionalis.* Reticulated head-pattern. Specimen from Vietnam. Length 20 cm. Atsushi Morioka.

Chaetodontoplus cephalareticulatus Shen & Lim, 1975.
NE coast of Taiwan.

Subtropical waters of Japan, probably ranging to mainland China coast and Taiwan, sympatric with *Chaetodontoplus septentrionalis* and often regarded as a variation of that species. The Maze

A

C. cephalareticulatus. Yokojima. D. 30 m. L. 16 cm. T. Hirata.

Angelfish occurs on shallow as well as deep reefs to about 35 m, and seems most common in the areas where corals become dominant on reefs, but ranges north to the rocky Izu peninsula, where *C. septentrionalis* is more common. Adults are yellow to orange on the head grading into the dark body, becoming black posteriorly, and have an irregular, 'maze-like' pattern of blue lines. Rear margins on the dorsal and anal fin, and caudal fin are yellow, rear margin of anal fin sometimes blue in large individuals. Juveniles black with yellow bands, and like in *C. melanosoma*, they develop a black submarginal tail band that fades when becoming subadult. Length to 24 cm.

Remarks: was until recently confused with the little-known *Chaetodontoplus chrysocephalus* and is part of a complex of species, together with *C. septentrionalis, C. chrysocephalus, C. dimidiatus, C. melanosoma* and *C. cf melanosoma*. Subadults, lacking any blue lines, have been confused with *C. melanosoma* from further south and it seems that this species does not actually occur in Taiwan or Japanese waters.

Aquarium: as for *Chaetodontoplus septentrionalis*.

B

C. cephalareticulatus. Kashiwajima, Japan. Depth 10 m. Length 16 cm. Tomonori Hirata.

C

C. cephalareticulatus. Izu Oceanic Park, Japan. Depth 15 m. Length 20 cm. Rudie Kuiter.

C. cephalareticulatus. Large juvenile, losing black marking in caudal fin. Kashiwajima. D. 4 m. L. 8 cm. Tomonori Hirata.

C. cephalareticulatus. Kochi, Japan. Depth 5 m. Length 22 cm. Tomonori Hirata.

C. cephalareticulatus. Japan. **F** IOP, aquarium. L. 35 mm. Hajime Masuda. **G** Kashiwajima. D. 8 m. L. 5 cm. Tomonori Hirata.

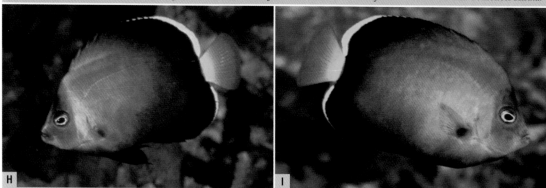

C. cephalareticulatus. Kashiwajima, Japan. **H** d. 10 m. L. 7 cm. **I** d. 5 m. L. 8 cm. Tomonori Hirata.

C. cephalareticulatus. Japan. **J** Kashiwajima. D. 20 m. L. 16 cm. Tomonori Hirata.**K** IOP, aquarium. Hiroshi Senou.

C. cephalareticulatus. Kashiwajima, Japan. **L** d. 25 m. L. 18 cm. **M** d. 5 m. L. 18 cm. Tomonori Hirata.

C. cephalareticulatus. On a soft-coral wall. Yokojima, Japan. Tomonori Hirata.

C. cephalareticulatus. Aquarium, collected off Kochi Prefecture, Shikoku. Length 20 cm. Yukio Aramata.

A

C. chrysocephalus. Juv. from Philippines. L. 9 cm. Hiroyuki Tanaka.

Blue Vermiculate Angelfish
Chaetodontoplus chrysocephalus

Holacanthus chrysocephalus Bleeker, 1854. Java.
Syn: *Chaetodontoplus caeruleopunctatus*
Yasuda & Tominaga, 1976. Philippines.

A rarely observed species that is only known from the Java Sea and Cebu, Philippines. Shipments from latter are not rare, but they are usually juveniles or subadults. The adults may prefer deep water, whilst as a species it may be habitat-specific, perhaps feeding on certain sponges or other sessile invertebrate varieties. This species is identified by the bright yellow tail; numerous tiny blue spots that join into scribbles and lines on the head in large adults and run into the yellow of the caudal fin; white margin and blue submarginal lines on the dorsal and anal fins; and it has a blue-edged black ocellus on the pectoral-fin base. Length to 20 cm.

Remarks: this species was previously referred to as *Chaetodontoplus caeruleopunctatus*, however, *C. chrysocephalus* is an older name for the same species. The descriptions were based on a juvenile (70 mm) and a male (170 mm) respectively, and are here placed in synonymy. The name *C. chrysocephalus* is often used in Japan for *C. cephalareticulatus*, a similar species from Taiwan and Japan.

Aquarium: sometimes difficult to keep, due to refusal of any kind of food. This may be because of a special diet requirement, unless some Philippine collectors still use cyanide, which damages vital organs and usually causes a delayed death (few months).

B

C. chrysocephalus. Aquarium. L. 12 cm. Frank Schneidewind.

C

C. chrysocephalus. Probable female. Cebu, Philippines. Depth 28 m. Length 18 cm. Kazunori (GARUDA) Igarashi.

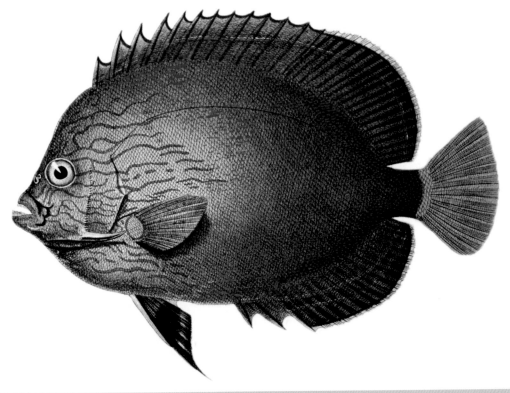

C. chrysocephalus. Illustration of Bleekers type from Java. Length 17 cm. After Bleeker.

C. chrysocephalus. Probable male. Karimunjawa, Java, Indonesia. Depth 22 m. Length 20 cm. Takamasa Tonozuka.

Black Velvet Angelfish *Chaetodontoplus melanosoma*

Holacanthus melanosoma Bleeker, 1853. Solor I. Indonesia.

Western Pacific, Philippines and Indonesia. Occurs on coastal and outer reef slopes at moderate depths to 30 m, usually in strong current habitats where holding up in caves. In Indonesia this species is recorded from Bali from where it ranges east to Flores and Solor Island, and north via the Wallace's Line to the Philippines. Records from elsewhere are not this, but similar species. Adults are almost completely black and feature a thin yellow margin posteriorly on the median fins. The head and part of the upper body is somewhat paler than the rest of the body. Juveniles have a black band on the caudal fin that gradually reduces with growth, whilst the black of the body creeps onto the caudal fin. Distinguished from the similar *Chaetodontoplus dimidiatus* in having a mostly black versus completely yellow tail and body colouration. Often shipped from the Philippines. Fully grown individuals are rather difficult to acclimatise in the home aquarium, but juveniles or subadults could be kept for a long period. Attains a length of 20 cm.

Remarks: Sometimes called Phantom Angelfish but this name should be applied to the very similar *Chaetodontoplus dimidiatus*. A separate population, that now appears to be a distinct species, occurring in Milne Bay, Papua New Guinea.

C. melanosoma. **A** Bali, Indonesia. D. 23 m. L. 22 mm. Takamasa Tonozuka. **B** Mabul, Malaysia. D. 25 m. L. 20 mm. Rudie Kuiter.

C. melanosoma. Aquarium. Philippine specimen. Length 15 cm. Rudie Kuiter.

C. melanosoma. Bali, Indonesia. Depth 25 m. Length 20 cm. Rudie Kuiter.

C. melanosoma. Bali, Indonesia. Depth 25 m. Length 20 cm. Rudie Kuiter.

Pale-head Velvet Angelfish
Chaetodontoplus cf *melanosoma*
Undetermined species.

Only known from south-eastern Papua New Guinea, mainly Milne Bay. Occurs in sheltered bays and various solitary individuals have been observed in depths between 5 and 30 m. Adults are mostly black, the head pales to almost white and the posterior margins of the dorsal, anal and caudal fins are bright yellow. Juveniles are jet-black with yellow bands, and the caudal fin has a narrow black submarginal band that widens with growth, eventually filling the tail until leaving a bright yellow posterior margin. Length to at least 20 cm.

Remarks: this species is most similar to *Chaetodontoplus melanosoma*, its closest relative. It differs from that species in colour in both juvenile and adult stages. In *C. melanosoma* the head-band is almost white and the black submarginal tail-band fades with growth whilst black from the body spreads onto the tail. In *C. melanosoma* the head is dark grey.

Aquarium: probably like other velvet angelfishes, but lives in shallower depths and may be less difficult with regards to food or shyness.

C. cf *melanosoma*. Juvenile. Milne Bay, PNG. Scott Michael.

C. cf *melanosoma*. Pair in habitat. Milne Bay, PNG. Depth 10 m. Length 20 cm. Bob Halstead.

C. cf *melanosoma*. Milne Bay, PNG. Depth 10 m. Length 20 cm. Neville Coleman.

Phanthom Angelfish *Chaetodontoplus dimidiatus*

Holacanthus dimidiatus Bleeker, 1860. Ambon. Indonesia.

Indonesia, northeastern Sulawesi, Moluccas, Halmahera and north-western Irian Jaya. Probably restricted to this limited range. Adult *Chaetodontoplus dimidiatus* usually lives on current prone, semi-open reef flats with a rich growth of sessile invertebrates, such as gorgonians and seawhips, at depths of 35+ m. They swim openly about and are usually in pairs. Juveniles solitary in sheltered coastal bays in 10–15 m. Adults are pale grey, almost white, on upper half of body with the rest darker, changing abruptly mid-laterally whilst the tail is all yellow. Juveniles are black with pale yellow to white bands. Will reach over 22 cm.

Remarks: appears to be allopatric from the closely related and similar looking *Chaetodontoplus melanosoma* and *C.* cf *melanosoma*. The three species have been confused by most people, but whilst adults can be distinguished by their colour pattern, small juveniles are virtually identical.

Aquarium: requirements are probably similar to *Chaetodontoplus melanosoma*, but it lives in a different habitat and may be more demanding with regards to food and have a preference for dark areas.

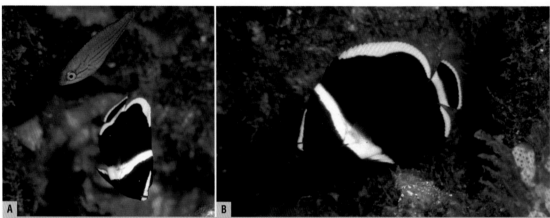

C. dimidiatus. Lembeh Strait, Sulawesi, Indonesia. Depth 15 m. Length 20 mm. Rudie Kuiter.

C. dimidiatus. Lembeh Strait, Sulawesi, Indonesia. Depth 35 m. Length 22 cm. Rudie Kuiter.

C. dimidiatus. Indonesia. **D** Halmahera. D. 52 m. L. 20 cm. Helmut Debelius. **E** Sulawesi. D. 35 m. L. 17 cm. Rudie Kuiter.

C. dimidiatus. Travelling pair. Lembeh Strait, Sulawesi, Indonesia. Depth 35 m. Length 22 cm. Rudie Kuiter.

Chaetodontoplus meredithi Kuiter, 1990. Sydney Harbour.

Eastern Australia from far north Queensland to the Sydney region of New South Wales. Occurs on coastal and inner reefs, usually in sponge and seawhip habitats and adults feed primarily on sponges. Large adults usually on deep reefs, at 30 m or more. Juveniles are often in shallow protected harbours and bays. Adults with dark bluish-black covering from caudal peduncle, dorsal and anal fins to dorsal origin above and pectoral fin and almost reaching ventral fins below, then abruptly changing to a pale colour, and yellow tail. The head is mostly blue and adorned with numerous yellow spots, yellow over nape, followed by a plain pale band that ranges from pure white to pale blue. Pectoral fin mostly black with yellow margin. Juveniles are mostly black with a yellow tail and ventral fins and a white head-band behind the eye. Length to at least 25 cm.

Remarks: closely related to *Chaetodontoplus personifer*, but adults of that species have a broad black band on the caudal fin or are nearly all black.

Aquarium: adults will not easily adapt to captivity. Juveniles are much easier to acclimate, the smaller the better.

C. meredithi. Aquarium. Sydney specimens. **A** length 30 mm. **B** length 75 mm. Rudie Kuiter.

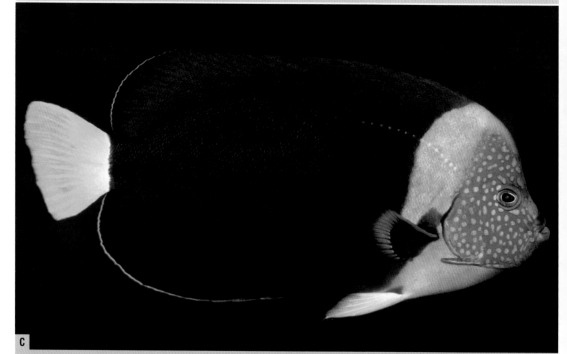

C. meredithi. Male. Keppel Island, Queensland. Depth 15 m. Length 25 cm. Rudie Kuiter.

D

C. meredithi. Subadult. Moreton Bay, southern Queensland. Depth 15 m. Length 15 cm. Rudie Kuiter.

E

C. meredithi. Probable female. Keppel Island, Queensland. Depth 15 m. Length 23 cm. Rudie Kuiter.

C. meredithi. **F** Sydney, Australia. D. 3 m. L. 25 mm. Rudie Kuiter. **G** Great Barrier Reef, D. 10 m. L. 14 cm. Helmut Debelius.

C. meredithi. Large adults, feeding on sponge on the famous Heron I. bommie, Great Barrier Reef. Bill Wood.

Personifer Angelfish
Chaetodontoplus personifer

Chaetodontoplus personifer McCulloch, 1914. Western Australia.

North-western Australia, from the Houtman Abrolhos to off the Kimberley coast. Occurs on shallow inshore reefs and rocky habitats to depths of about 40 m. Adults mostly black with pale grey to blue head and caudal fin with small-moon shaped yellow margin. Males are proportionally longer than females. Juveniles are black with a yellow tail and white headband behind the eye. Length to 35 cm.

Remarks: Taiwan reports are based on market specimens, together with *Chaetodontoplus duboulayi*, no doubt captured from Western Australia. Adults and juveniles very similar to the closely related *C. meredithi* from the eastern Australian coast. Adults are best distinguished by the black band or mostly black area in the tail.

Aquarium: adults are difficult to keep and need to be provided with sponges and tunicates, while juveniles are less demanding.

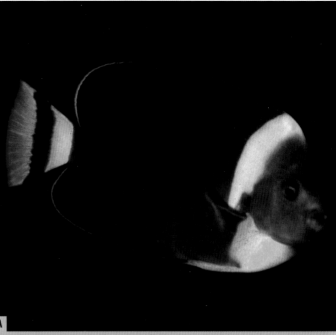

A

C. personifer. North West Cape. Depth 15 m. Length 14 cm. Jerry Allen.

B

C. personifer. Adult male. Exmouth, Western Australia. Length 25 cm. Scott Michael.

A

Ballina Angelfish *Chaetodontoplus ballinae*
Chaetodontoplus ballinae Whitley, 1959.
Off Ballina, NSW, Australia.

Lord Howe Island & northern NSW, Australia. Inhabits deep coral and rocky reefs from about 25 m down. At Lord Howe Island, a population lives on a sea-mound, about 25 m below the surface, where they pair and swim openly about, sometimes taking refuge below *Acropora* coral plates, which grow there at a moderate depth due to the pristine oceanic conditions. Usually observed in pairs but sometimes in small loose groups of three or more individuals. Adult colour purely white with an L-shaped broad black band on upper half of body to pectoral base. Has black lips, yellow around eyes, and bright yellow pectoral and caudal fins. Juveniles are not known. Length to at least 20 cm.

Remarks: only two specimens, 19 & 20 cm long, were known until 1994. First specimen was collected in 1959 in a deep-water fish trap off Ballina, northern New South Wales. The second specimen was captured in 1978 in a deep-water trawl at a depth of 120 m off NSW. In the 1990's a population was discovered near Lord Howe Island. Sightings of unusual angelfish by divers off NSW may be contributed to this species and hopefully will be photographed in the near future.

Aquarium: no information on aquarium care is available. Due to its small population these fishes should not be collected from the wild. In addition, this species is fully protected and cannot be collected legally without a permit, which will not be issued for aquarium exports. Lord Howe Island is a World Heritage zone.

B

C

C. ballinae. Lord Howe Island, Australia. Depth 25 m. Length 20 cm. Neville Coleman.

D

C. ballinae. Lord Howe Island, Australia. Depth 25 m. Length 20 cm. Neville Coleman.

E

C. ballinae. Sharing habitat with *C. conspicillatus.* Lord Howe Island, Australia. Depth 20 m. Tsuneo Nakamura.

Scribbled Angelfish *Chaetodontoplus duboulayi*

Holacanthus duboulayi Günther,1867. Nw Australia.

Tropical Australian waters, ranging to southern New Guinea and nearby islands of Indonesia. Occurs on coral rich substrates, usually found shallower than 20 metres, but also known from trawled specimens from continental shelf. Adults are dark blue with a very broad vertical yellow band behind the eye (has white area behind eye, especially in males) from below dorsal origin to abdomen, joined by a distinct curving yellow band on back continuing onto caudal peduncle. Mouth and caudal fin yellow. Males busily marked with fine blue stripes, while females are plain dusky or covered with fine blue speckles. Juveniles similar to adults. Adults occur in small loose groups. Length to about 26 cm, rarely larger.

Remarks: records from Taiwan are based on fish-market specimens that were most likely taken from Australian waters.

Aquarium: juveniles are easily kept and recommended for beginner aquarists. Adults may adapt more easily compared to their congeners. In the wild it is common in algae reef habitats and may be more flexible in its food requirements.

C. duboulayi. Keppel Island, southern Queensland, Australia. Depth 15 m. Lengths: **A** 20 cm. **B** 75 mm. Rudie Kuiter.

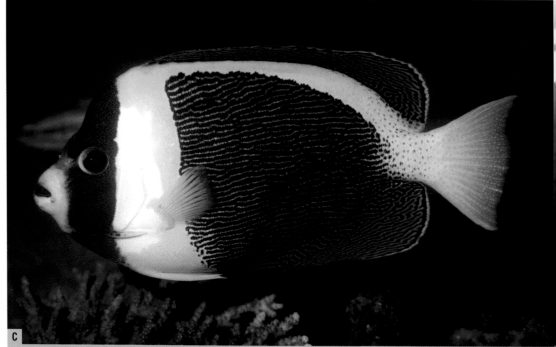

C. duboulayi. Large male. Keppel Island, southern Queensland, Australia. Depth 15 m. Length 26 cm. Rudie Kuiter.

D

C. duboulayi. Keppel Island, southern Queensland, Australia. Depth 15 m. Length 22 cm. Rudie Kuiter.

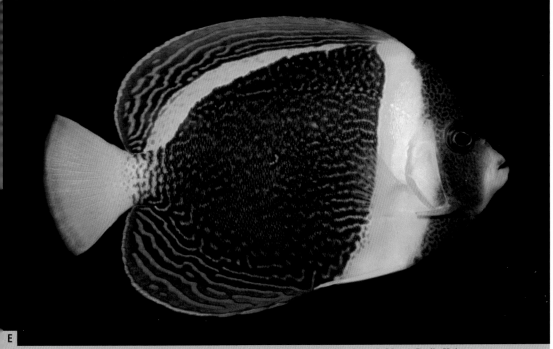

E

C. duboulayi. Aquarium. Specimen from Queensland, Australia. Length 20 cm. Rudie Kuiter.

Spectacled Angelfish
Chaetodontoplus conspicillatus

Holacanthus conspicillatus Waite, 1900.
Lord Howe Island.

Southern Queensland to Lord Howe & Norfolk Islands & New Caledonia with expatriates as far south as Sydney. Adults inhabit coral-rich outer reef slopes at depths of about 20 to 40 m, but may venture much shallower. Juveniles are usually in the shallows of lagoons and harbours at depths of about 2–10 m. Adults are readily identified by their yellow face with a distinct blue ring encircling each eye and blue margins on the preoperculum and operculum. Mouth white with black band behind, ventral fins white, and median fins have bluish white edges. Pectorals and caudal fins are yellow at the base with broad black outer parts. Small juveniles are black with a white dorsal fin and have a thin white band on their otherwise clear caudal fin. With growth, the caudal fin becomes black and a yellow or white band develops near its base, whilst the upper sides of the body pales to a brown-orange colour. Elongated adults are thought to be males. Length to 25 cm.

Remarks; unusual member of the genus, showing some similarities with *Chaetodontoplus niger* from the northern Western Pacific.

Aquarium; both adults and juveniles are expensive aquarium fish, but are fairly good community fish. Introduced adults may refuse food and this species will probably nip on live corals.

C. conspicillatus. Lord Howe I., Australia. D. 22 m. L. 24 cm. Neville Coleman.

C. conspicillatus. Aquarium. Sydney specimens. Lengths **C** 9 mm. **D** 20 mm. **E** 60 mm. **F** 95 mm. Rudie Kuiter.

C. conspicillatus. Malabar, Lord Howe Island, Australia. Length ~22 cm. Malcolm Francis.

Black Angelfish *Chaetodontoplus niger*

Chaetodontoplus niger Chan, 1969.
Macclesfield Bank, South China Seas

Only known from a few scattered localities in south China Sea and southern Japan: Okinawa, Kashiwajima, Wakayama and Izu Peninsula. A rarely observed deep water species, but several were sighted in Japanese waters and in the Izu Peninsula it was observed as shallow as 17 metres during mid winter. Also divers photographed it recently in Kashiwajima, Shikoku (March, 1998), eastern Izu Peninsula (February, 1998) and Kumejima (2002). All were observed feeding on the rock surfaces which in deep water are usually covered with low sessile invertebrates and coralline algae. Appears to be shy and difficult to photograph. Easily identified by its almost black colour and the conspicuous white ventral fins and yellow tail. Juveniles and adults are similar, with adults becoming more elongate. May reach a length of 35 cm.

Remarks: described from a single juvenile, 65 mm long, taken in 70–80 m. Chan, its describer, suspected that it might only be a junior synonym of *Chaetodontoplus melanosoma*, but a recent collection of three adult specimens from southern Honshu, Japan as trawled specimens revealed that it is a valid one.

Aquarium: none have been kept so far.

C. niger. Juvenile. Kumejima, Okinawa, Japan. Hiroshi Kobayashi.

C. niger. Juvenile. Kashiwajima, Japan. Depth 40 m. Length 35 mm. Tomonori Hirata.

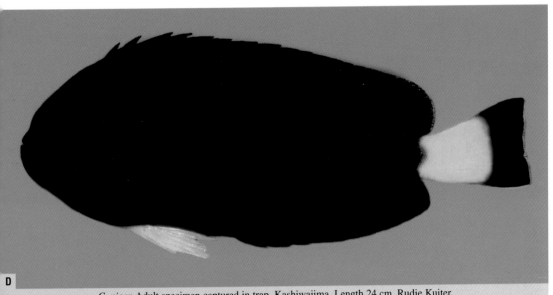

D

C. niger. Adult specimen captured in trap. Kashiwajima. Length 24 cm. Rudie Kuiter.

E

Locality of sightings and capture of *C. niger.* Kashiwajima, Japan. Photograph **C** at end of rocky outcrop. Rudie Kuiter.

Vermiculate Angelfish
Chaetodontoplus mesoleucus
Chaetodon mesoleucus Bloch, 1787. Japan.

Widespread Western Pacific from southern Japan to northern Australia, ranging to the west mainland Asian coast and into the Indian Ocean to southern Sumatra, whilst in the east to at least Irian Jaya*. Occurs in coral rich areas in lagoons or coastal reefs, shallow to about 20 m deep. Adults normally in pairs, whilst subadults sometimes aggregate in small groups and juveniles solitary. Diet comprises algae, sponges and tunicates. Adults and juveniles are similar and recognised by their eye-band (as seen in butterflyfishes), followed by white that grades into black and a bright yellow tail. The snout is yellow whilst lips and dorsal and anal fin margins are blue. The sexes seem identical in colour. Reaches 18 cm.

C. mesoleucus. Sulawesi, Indonesia. D. 10 m. L. 17 cm. Rudie Kuiter.

Remarks: *recorded east to the Solomon Islands and southern Papua New Guinea, but this needs to be confirmed as it may be based on the similar Grey-tail Angelfish that occurs there, an undescribed species confused with *Chaetodontoplus mesoleucus*.

Aquarium: juveniles are commonly encountered during the summer by Japanese divers and collectors in shallow waters of the Ryukyu Islands. An easy fish to keep and commonly found in the marine-fish trade in Japan. The author HT kept this species for one and a half years without any problems.

C. mesoleucus. **B** Java, Indonesia. D. 5 m. L 20 mm. Rudie Kuiter. **C** Yaeyama, Japan. L. ~16 mm. Hajime Masuda.

C. mesoleucus. Flores, Indonesia. Depth 15 m. Length 16 cm. Rudie Kuiter.

E

C. mesoleucus. Pair. Bali, Indonesia. Depth 20 m. Length 16 cm. Rudie Kuiter.

F

C. mesoleucus. Group of subadults, *Chaetodon falcula* above. Sumatra, Indonesia. D. 12 m. Lengths ~10 cm. Helmut Debelius.

A

C. cf *mesoleucus.* Flores, Indonesia. D. 25 m. L. 16 cm. Rudie Kuiter.

B

C. cf *mesoleucus.* Flores, Indonesia. D. 25 m. L. 16 cm. Rudie Kuiter.

Grey-tail Angelfish
Chaetodontoplus cf *mesoleucus*

Undescribed species

Known from southern Indonesia, Bali to Flores, and Papua New Guinea to the Solomon Islands and Palau. Lives in rich coral areas, mainly on deep slopes of fringing coastal reefs. Adults at depths of about 20 m and nearly always in pairs. Subadults higher on slopes, usually at 10–20 m depth. In Flores it is common and the similar *Chaetodontoplus mesoleucus* is just as common on the same reefs. It was here, where the third author recognised the grey-tailed species to be a different species. No interaction was observed and meeting pairs did not show any interest in each other. No mixed pairs of the two species were ever seen and this was constantly checked by the third author during his hundreds of dives in Maumere Bay, Flores. Since both species are common there, it is unlikely that hybrids occur. This species seems to be slightly smaller than *C. mesoleucus,* growing to about 16 cm.

Remarks: a poorly known species that has been confused with *Chaetodontoplus mesoleucus* which is identical in shape and has a similar colouration, but when comparing the two, there are significant differences. Most obvious is the grey versus yellow caudal fin and the yellow versus white ventral fins. It further differs in the shape of the head band and even the actual body colouration. Large individuals are elongate as found in several other congeners, thought to be males, and these are also much more grey on the posterior section of the body.

Aquarium: food requirements are probably the same as for *Chaetodontoplus mesoleucus.*

C

C. cf *mesoleucus.* Subadult. Flores, Indonesia. Depth 10 m. Length 12 cm. Rudie Kuiter.

C. cf *mesoleucus.* Flores, Indonesia. Depth 20 m. Length 16 cm. Rudie Kuiter.

C. cf *mesoleucus.* Flores, Indonesia. Depth 20 m. Length 16 cm. Rudie Kuiter.

GENUS *Pygoplites* Fraser-Brunner, 1933

Masculine. Type species. *Chaetodon diacanthus* Boddaert, 1772. Monotypic, but comprises a widespread species with distinct forms between the populations in the Pacific and those in the Indian Ocean and Red Sea.

Regal Angelfish *Pygoplites diacanthus*

Chaetodon diacanthus Boddaert, 1772. Ambon

Indo-West Pacific, ranging from Red Sea and east coast of Africa, through most Indian Ocean islands to Western Pacific from Japan to Australia and Pacific east to the Tuamotu Archipelago. Occurs in coral-rich lagoons on shallow reef flats and along walls near caves or ledges to depths of 80 m where they feed primarily on certain sponges.

Juveniles secretive in caves and usually seen solitary. Adults in pairs and occasionally in small groups. Readily identified by the patterns of many alternating orange, blue and white vertical stripes. Two distinct colour variations between Pacific and Indian Ocean. Most obvious in adults is the grey (Pacific) versus yellow (Indian) chest. Being more colourful in general makes the Indian Ocean form more popular amongst aquarists. Juveniles are similar to adults, but feature a distinct ocellus at the rear of the base of the dorsal fin. Aberrations in the striped pattern are quite common and occasionally yellow-looking individuals, lacking dark pigments, are sighted in both the Indian and Pacific Oceans. Length to 25 cm.

Remarks: In Japan they are common in the Ryukyus but rarely seen in southern Honshu, and are also fairly common in Hachijoh-jima, the Izu Islands, but very rare in Ogasawara. Not reported from Oman or Mauritius.

Aquarium: adults do not usually accept any food when introduced to an aquarium, but young may readily accept food. Some adults may accept live sponges or tunicates at first and over time convert to other foods, but once acclimatised they can live for a long time. Because of this, adults are often sold at lower prices than juveniles (Japan). Not an aggressive fish and can be kept with damselfishes, butterflyfishes and safely with larger angelfishes, but may harm some species of corals or ornamental shrimps in reef tanks. A great eye-catching addition to any aquarium.

A

P. diacanthus. Flores, Indonesia. D. 25 m. L. 40 mm. Rudie Kuiter.

B

P. diacanthus. Bali, Indonesia. D. 15 m. L. 25 cm. Rudie Kuiter.

P. diacanthus. Juveniles **C** Sipadan, Malaysia. Depth 30 m. Length 30 mm. Rudie Kuiter. **D** Bali, Indonesia. Mark Strickland.

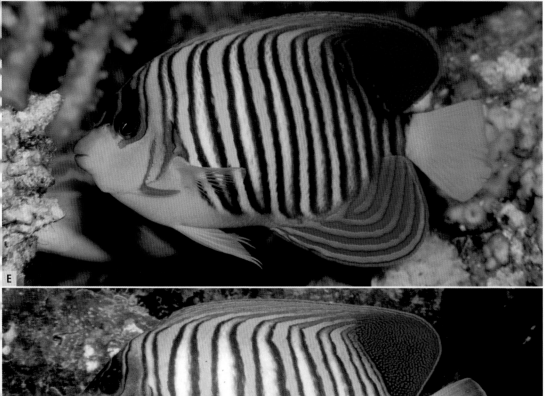

P. diacanthus. Indian & Pacific forms. Lengths 20 cm. **E** Red Sea. D. 15 m. **F** Queensland, Australia. D. 12 m. Rudie Kuiter.

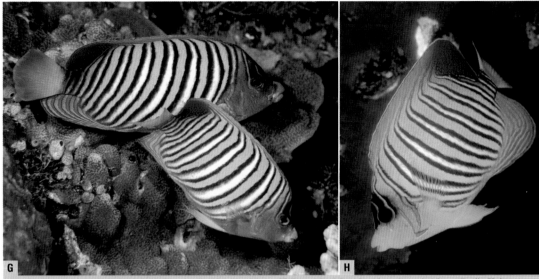

P. diacanthus. **G** Sangihe I., Indonesia. D. 15 m. L. 25 cm. **H** Egypt, Red Sea. D. 12 m. Length 15 cm. Rudie Kuiter.

P. diacanthus. Cook Islands, South Pacific. Depth 12 m. Length 15 cm. Helmut Debelius.

P. diacanthus. Maldives. **J** depth 10 m. Length 25 cm. **K** depth 15 m. Length 16 cm. Rudie Kuiter.

P. diacanthus. Aberrant pattern (other side normal). Flores, Indonesia. Depth 20 m. Length 24 cm. Rudie Kuiter.

P. diacanthus. Colour morphs. **M** & **N** Maldives depth 20 m. Length 20 cm. Rudie Kuiter. **O** Solomon Islands. Astrid Witte.

GENUS *Genicanthus* Swainston, 1839

Masculine. Type species: *Holacanthus lamarck* Lacepède, 1802. Comprises 10 species. Their distribution is the Indo-West Pacific, and the Red Sea. Most occur in the Philippines-Indonesian region, one in the Red Sea, and some are restricted to remote, subtropical regions of the Pacific. These swallow-tailed angelfishes are primarily planktivorous and feed in open water, often several metres above the seabed in pursuit of food, ready to seek shelter when danger approaches. Their habitat is often along deep outer reef walls where currents carry the oceanic plankton, and most species live at moderate depths, rarely seen at depths less than 20 m, but some rise from deep water to feed when food is abundant at shallower depths.

Amongst angelfishes, sexual dimorphism is exceptionally remarkable. Usually males are much more colourful than their partners and often feature long filaments on their caudal fin. All are born as females but after reaching maturity some of them change sex, activating the male sex organs and changing colour and morphology at the same time. Normally they live in small aggregations, comprising a small number of females and one dominating male. In such a harem-like arrangement some of the females have the potential to change sex, but this is suppressed by the presence of the male. If the male drops out, usually the largest female becomes dominant in the group and then changes sex. The various species range in maximum size from about 20 cm to 35 cm, excluding filamentous rays. Males are typically larger than females and have elaborate patterns of lines, stripes or dots, while females are generally rather plain. All species prefer open spaces and good hiding places and the larger the aquarium, the better. These fishes are known to jump and the aquarium should be well covered. A number of individuals can be kept together, starting with a few females, and the sex-change of one of them is likely to take place in the aquarium.

List of species. Genus *Genicanthus*

1.	*G. bellus*	*Genicanthus bellus* Randall, 1975. Tahiti. (p. **142**)
2.	*G. caudovittatus*	*Holacanthus caudovittatus* Günther, 1860. Mauritius. (p. **146**)
3.	*G. lamarck*	*Holacanthus lamarck* Lacepéde, 1802. No locality. (p. **140**)
4.	*G. melanospilos*	*Holacanthus melanospilos* Bleeker, 1857. Ambon. (p. **143**)
5.	*G. personatus*	*Genicanthus personatus* Randall, 1975. Hawaiian Isands. (p. **158**)
6.	*G. semicinctus*	*Holacanthus semicinctus* Waite, 1900. Lord Howe Island. (p. **150**)
7.	*G. semifasciatus*	*Holacanthus semifasciatus* Kamohara, 1934. Kochi Pref., Japan. (p. **148**)
8.	*G. spinus*	*Genicanthus spinus* Randall, 1975. Pitcairn I. (p. **152**)
9.	*G. takeuchii*	*Genicanthus takeuchii* Pyle, 1997. Ogasawara Is., Japan. (p. **155**)
10.	*G. watanabei*	*Holacanthus watanabei* Yasuda & Tominaga, 1970. Okinawa, Japan. (p. **153**)

G. lamarck. Male. Type for genus with typical swallow-tail and filamentous tips. Flores, Indonesia. Rudie Kuiter.

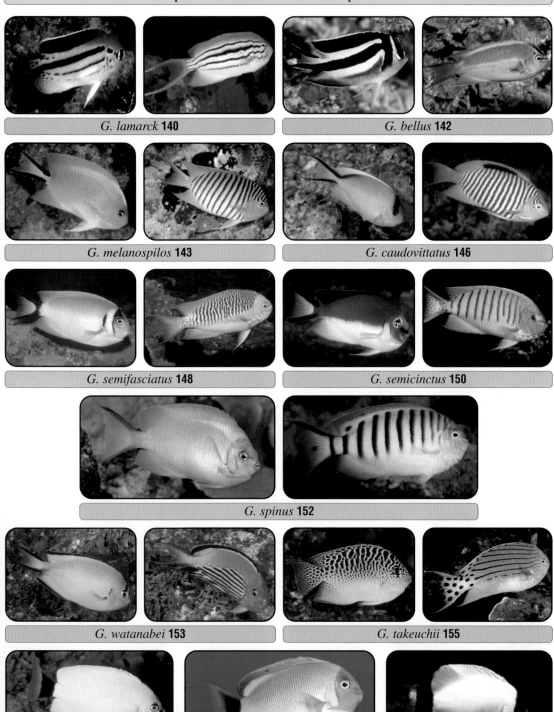

G. lamarck **140**

G. bellus **142**

G. melanospilos **143**

G. caudovittatus **146**

G. semifasciatus **148**

G. semicinctus **150**

G. spinus **152**

G. watanabei **153**

G. takeuchii **155**

G. personatus **158**

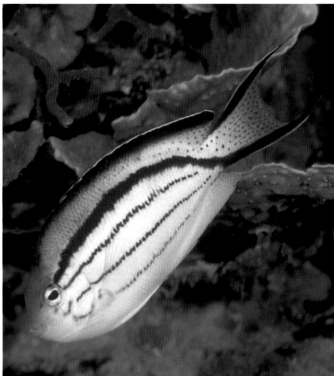

Lamarck's Angelfish
Genicanthus lamarck

Holacanthus lamarck Lacepède, 1802. No locality.

Widespread Western Pacific, from the Ryukyu Is of southern Japan to the northern Great Barrier Reef, southeast to Vanuatus, and west to Sumatra, Indonesia). Absent from most oceanic locations in the Pacific. Occurs primarily on seaward reef slopes and steep walls, or in protected areas to at least 50 m depth. Sometimes on very shallow reef crests of a few metres depth. Both sexes are similar in appearance, being silvery white with three or four horizontal black stripes on the side and a broad black submarginal band in the dorsal fin. Upper stripe in female is usually thick and continues down onto the lower caudal fin lobe. Males have black ventral fins and white caudal fin lobes, whilst the female has white ventral fins and black caudal fin lobes. Males also have a yellow spot on top of the forehead, and develop very long upper and lower caudal-fin lobes. Both sexes have numerous black dots on caudal fin, some also on anal and dorsal fins. Attains 23 cm.

Remarks: a record from African coast is without doubt a misidentification.

Aquarium: somewhat difficult to maintain but can live for a long period when starting off with a small juvenile stage.

A

G. lamarck. Female. Flores, Indonesia. D. 25 m. L. 15 cm. Rudie Kuiter.

B

G. lamarck. Male. Flores, Indonesia. D. 10 m. L. 22 cm. Rudie Kuiter.

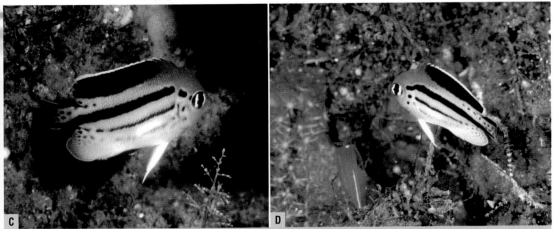

G. lamarck. Small juveniles. Bali, Indonesia. D. 30 m. L. 35 mm. Rudie Kuiter.

G. lamarck. Females. **E.** aquarium. Thick-striped, no locality. Length 12 cm. **F** Bali, Indonesia. D. 20 m. L. 15 cm. Rudie Kuiter.

G. lamarck. Male. Milne Bay, Papua New Guinea. D. 15 m. L. 22 cm. Rudie Kuiter.

A

G. bellus. Aquarium. Female from Indonesia. Fenton Walsh.

Ornate Angelfish *Genicanthus bellus*

Genicanthus bellus Randall, 1975. Tahiti.

Known from scattered localities in the Pacific, from southern Japan and Micronesia to southern Indonesia and Tahiti, and Cocos-Keeling Atoll in the eastern Indian Ocean. Inhabits areas adjacent to steep outer reef slopes between 25–100 m, usually seen deeper than 50 m. A very beautifully marked angelfish in both sexes. Females and juveniles are boldly marked with black and white and a curving streak of blue on lower sides. Males feature two orange-yellow horizontal bands running dorsally and mid-laterally on the body. Attains 15 cm excluding filamentous rays.

Remarks: unlike most other angelfishes, females may be larger at maturity than males, but latter still grows largest. Due to deep water preference, they are rarely observed in the wild by divers, especially males, as females outnumber males greatly, often by about five or more to one.

Aquarium: fairly easy to keep in aquaria, but sensitive to poor water quality, resulting in refusal of food. They may jump out of the aquarium when disturbed. Females are regularly exported from the Philippines, but males are rarely seen in the aquarium trade.

B

C

G. bellus. **B** large female. Cocos-Keeling. D. 45 m. Michale Moxter. **C** juvenile. Okinawa, Japan. D. 55 m. Hiroshi Kobayashi.

D

G. bellus. Male. Papeete, Tahiti. Depth 42 m. Philippe Bacchet.

Black-spot Angelfish *Genicanthus melanospilos*

Holacanthus melanospilos Bleeker, 1847. Ambon.

Widespread Western Pacific, ranging from Southern Japan to northern Australia, including the Rowley Shoals off north-western Australia, and Coral Sea to Fiji. Prefers steep outer reef slopes and drop-offs, usually at depths greater than 20 m and ranges to at least 50 m. Usually found in small groups or in pairs. Males bluish white with many thin vertical stripes over top of head and along entire body, and a black spot on the chest from which it gets its name. Females with yellow upper sides that gradually change to bluish white ventrally and black caudal-fin lobes. Length to 18 cm, excluding caudal filaments.

Remarks: closely related to *Genicanthus caudovittatus* from the Red Sea and Indian Ocean, sharing similar colour patterns of both sexes, including the males' dark spot on the chest.

Aquarium: difficult to keep large males in a home aquarium, but smaller ones can be successfully kept for a long time.

A

G. melanospilos. Juv. Bali, Indonesia. Takamasa Tonozuka.

B

G. melanospilos. Very large female (largest ever seen). Kalimantan, Indonesia. D. 35 m. L. 18 cm. Rudie Kuiter.

C

G. melanospilos. Male. Flores, Indonesia. Depth 35 m. Length 18 cm. Rudie Kuiter.

D

G. melanospilos. Male. Rowley Shoals, off north-western Australia. Depth 50 m. Length 18 cm. Rudie Kuiter.

E

G. melanospilos. Female. Rowley Shoals, off north-western Australia. Depth 50 m. Length 16 cm. Rudie Kuiter.

144

G. melanospilos. **F** male. Rowley Shoals, WA, Australia. **G** female. Flores, Indonesia. Depth 35 m. Length 15 cm. Rudie Kuiter.

G. melanospilos. Male, showing the black 'chest' spot. Flores, Indonesia. Depth 35 m. Length 18 cm. Rudie Kuiter.

G. caudovittatus. Female, 15 cm. Egypt, Red Sea. Rudie Kuiter.

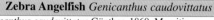

Zebra Angelfish *Genicanthus caudovittatus*

Holacanthus caudovittatus Günther, 1860. Mauritius.

Widespread Western Indian Ocean, south to the Aliwal Shoal, South Africa, and Red Sea to Sumatra. Occurs on coral rich seaward reef slopes or steep drop-offs at depths of 15–70 m. In the Red Sea it is more shallow, to about 35 m, while in Sumatra and South Africa it prefers deeper water below 40 m. Usually seen in pairs or in small groups with a dominant male and several females, forming a harem. Males white with many vertical dark stripes, prominent black spot on chest and a black band on base of dorsal fin. Females have a bluish-grey black band above eye when small, and black caudal-fin lobes. Length to 20 cm.

Remarks: differs from the similar *Genicanthus melanospilos* in colour. Females lack yellow on the back and males have a yellow and black band on the spinous part of the dorsal fin. Juveniles similar to damselfish, perhaps mimicking them.

Aquarium: large individuals often refuse food in captivity, and it is best to try them with brine shrimps first.

G. caudovittatus. Male & femeale. Aliwal Shoal, South Africa. Depth 40 m. Length 20 & 18 cm. Rudie Kuiter.

G. caudovittatus. Male. Egypt, Red Sea. Depth 20 m. Length 20 cm. Rudie Kuiter.

G. caudovittatus. Juvenile. Mauritius. Hugues Vitry.

G. caudovittatus. Pulau Weh, Sumatra, Indonesia. Depth 40–45 m. **J** juvenile 45 mm. **K** female 15 cm. Takamasa Tonozuka.

G. caudovittatus. Females. Egypt, Red Sea. Depth 20 m. Length 12 cm. Rudie Kuiter.

G. caudovittatus. Aqaba, Jordan, Red Sea. **H** Male courting. **I** changed sex, starting to show male colours. Helmut Debelius.

Japanese Swallow
Genicanthus semifasciatus

Holacanthus semifasciatus Kamohara, 1934.
Kochi, Japan.

Restricted to the northwestern Pacific from southern Japan to Taiwan and the Philippines. Occurs on rocky reefs from about 15 m to very deep water. Reported at over 200 m. Sometimes seen in a harem-like group of a male with several females. Males are identified by the yellow-orange on the face that continues as a horizontal streak on the side with numerous narrow vertical dark lines above and plain white below. Females grey above, grading to white below, yellow along top of dorsal fin, a seahorse-shaped black band on eye, and black caudal lobes and peduncle. Length to 21 cm.

Remarks: it was first discovered in Miyake Island, the Izu Islands. Common in southern Izu Islands, while uncommon in Okinawa. The female form was described in 1970 as *Holacanthus fucosus* and treated as a separate species until 1975. A probable hybrid between *Genicanthus semifasciatus* and *G. melanospilos* was photographed in Ogasawara.

Aquarium: it seems to be a somewhat difficult species to keep in the home aquarium. As it rarely enters the aquarium trade, especially as small individuals, it demands a rather high price.

G. semifasciatus. Male. Okinawa, Japan. Hiroyuki Tatsuuma.

G. semifasciatus. Male. Japan. Hiroshi Takeuchi.

G. semifasciatus. Female. Japan. Hiroshi Takeuchi.

G. semifasciatus. Small female and juvenile. Hachijoh Island, Japan. Tomoyo Mizutani.

G. semifasciatus. Large female with cleaner wrasse *Labroides*. Hachijoh Island, Japan. Tomoyo Mizutani.

Half-banded Angelfish *Genicanthus semicinctus*

Genicanthus semicinctus Waite, 1900. Lord Howe Island.

Restricted to southwestern Pacific, Lord Howe Island, where fairly common, and Kermadec Islands, a rarely visited place where it is only known from a female photographed at 35 m depth in 1987. There are unconfirmed reports from New South Wales, Australia and this species is likely to occur in other adjacent areas such as Norfolk Island. Inhabits rocky reef slopes to at least 100 m depth. Usually occurs at depths over 30 m, but enters shallower waters in some localities and to feed, often around nearby sea-mounds. Males have mostly pale-grey upper sides with about ten vertical dark stripes, yellow below over belly and anal fin, and orange dorsally. Females are bluish black on upper half of body and purely white on lower side, have a blue interorbital area, and the caudal-fin lobes are black. A large species, length to at least 30 cm, excluding filamentous extensions on the caudal fin that can get very long.

Remarks: the 1900's original description was based on the male form, and the female was not known until 1973 when a large scientific team surveyed the fish fauna of Lord Howe Island. Closely related to *Genicanthus spinus* from the South Pacific, and only differ slightly in colour. Compared to *G. semicinctus,* females of *G. spinus* are more uniformly coloured and males have fewer spots on the caudal fin.

Aquarium: rarely seen in aquarium trade, demanding a high price. Due to feeding difficulties and the fact that it gets rather large, this species is best left in the wild. In addition, it is a protected species that primarily lives in a world-heritage zone, and any specimens appearing in the trade are likely to be illegal.

G. semicinctus. Male & juvenile. Lord Howe I. Malcolm Francis.

G. semicinctus. Female. Lord Howe I. Depth 20 m. Length 12 cm. Roger Steene.

G. semicinctus. Male. Lord Howe I. Neville Coleman.

G. semicinctus. Large female. Lord Howe I. Malcolm Francis.

G. semicinctus. Male. Lord Howe I. Jerry Allen.

Pitcairn Angelfish *Genicanthus spinus*

Genicanthus spinus Randall, 1975. Pitcairn.

South-east region of Pacific oceania, the Austral, Pitcairn and Cook Islands, east to Ducie Atoll. Lives primarily on outer reef slopes at 30–60 m depth or more. Colours of both sexes primarily pale bluish. Males cream on lower half of body with about eleven vertical dusky to black stripes above, continuing onto head where stripes become irregular. Area below head with pupil-sized dusky spots. One or a few distinct black spots in middle of caudal fin, and lobes reddish. Males develop exceptionally long filamentous extensions from the lobes on the caudal fin. Females plain pale bluish, lacking any marking on the head and body, except a short and narrow dark stripe on gill cover, although this description is based on freshly preserved material and in live specimens there are features, like the blue interorbital blue patch, that will be more obvious. Caudal lobes dark. Length to 35 cm, without long caudal filaments and males usually largest.

Remarks: closely related to *Genicanthus semicinctus* that has a more western distribution in the South Pacific, differing only slightly in the colour of both sexes.

Aquarium: first shipped to Japan in 1991. Almost no other record in the aquarium trade since then, but the specimens were too large to be kept successfully in the home aquarium due to its refusal of any food. No detailed aquarium information is yet available.

A

G. spinus. Female. Rapa. Yves Lefevre.

B

G. spinus. Aquarium. Male from Pitcairn. Richard Pyle.

Watanabe's Angelfish *Genicanthus watanabei*

Holacanthus watanabei Yasuda & Tominaga, 1970. Okinawa, Japan.

Widespread in the Western and Central Pacific, ranging from the Ryukyu and Ogasawara Islands, Taiwan to the Tuamotus; south to New Caledonia and the Austral Islands, also Palau, Marianas and Marshalls. Observed on steep outer reef slopes and drop-offs at depths that may be greater than 50 m in some areas, but much less in others like in the Coral Sea where as shallow as 20 m. Usually in small groups, comprising several females and a dominant male in a harem-like arrangement. Both sexes bluish-grey to blue. Males blue on upper half of body, and whitish ventrally with about 8–12 alternating black and white horizontal stripes, and a conspicuous yellow dash or stripe near caudal peduncle. Dark blue on caudal lobes. A black edge on dorsal and anal fins. Females pale blue, lacking any distinct markings on body, but have a black band above eye, a narrow dark stripe on upper part of gill cover, a black submarginal stripe on dorsal and anal fins, and black caudal-fin lobes. Length to 14 cm, excluding caudal filaments.

Remarks: not reported from the Philippines or Indonesia.

Aquarium: small individuals can be kept in home aquaria. Little else is known about their care.

G. *watanabei*. **A** female. Guam. Depth 55 m. Length 12 cm. Rudie Kuiter. **B** male. New Caledonia. Malcolm Francis.

G. *watanabei*. Large male. Coral Sea. Depth 20 m. Roger Steene.

153

D

G. watanabei. Male. Guam. Depth 55 m. Length 12 cm. Rudie Kuiter.

E

G. watanabei. Male left and female right. Guam. Depth 55 m. Length 12 & 10 cm. Rudie Kuiter.

Takeuchi's Angelfish *Genicanthus takeuchii*

Genicanthus takeuchii Pyle, 1997. Ogasawara Is., Japan.

Only known from the Marcus & Ogasawara Islands, southeastern Japan. Occurs on coral reef slopes that usually lay between 20 and 45 m, but the fish probably ranges much deeper. The habitat in the Ogasawara Islands is subject to strong tidal currents and cool upwellings of about 20°C, but the species appears to be more common at Minami Torishima (Marcus island) where they form small aggregations at depths of about 40 m. Such groups are females that are dominated by a single male. Juveniles live solitary. Both sexes are distinctly coloured. Males yellowish and whitish grey with several narrow longitudinal black lines over head and upper sides. Many black spots on caudal fin and end of dorsal fin that are diagnostic. Females are white ventrally, and grey dorsally with vermicular pattern of numerous fine spots that continues onto caudal fin. Juveniles bluish white with many close-set large black spots dorsally and numerous smaller dots below the larger ones and ventral area plain. The large black spots break up with growth, gradually changing into the female pattern. Caudal fin and posterior regions of dorsal and anal fins with many fine spots. Reaches 35 cm, one of the larger members in the genus.

Remarks: the species was named after Hiroshi Takeuchi, who first discovered it at Minami Tori Shima (Marcus Island) in 1987. Soon after it was also found in Chichi jima and Ani jima, the Ogasawara Islands.

Aquarium: this almost plain, but attractive fish has not yet entered the aquarium trade.

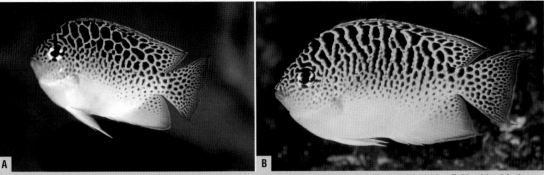

G. takeuchii. Juvenile and small female. Ogasawara Islands, Japan. Depth 30–40 m. **A** Osamu Morishita. **B** Yasuhiro Morita.

G. takeuchii. Male. Ogasawara Is, Japan. Hiroyuki Tatsuuma.

G. takeuchii. Small male. Minami Tori Shima, Japan. Depth 40 m. Hiroshi Takeuchi.

G. takeuchii. Group of females. Minami Torishima, Japan. Depth 40 m. Hiroshi Takeuchi.

F

G. takeuchii. Male. Ogasawara Islands, Japan. Depth 40 m. Osamu Morishita.

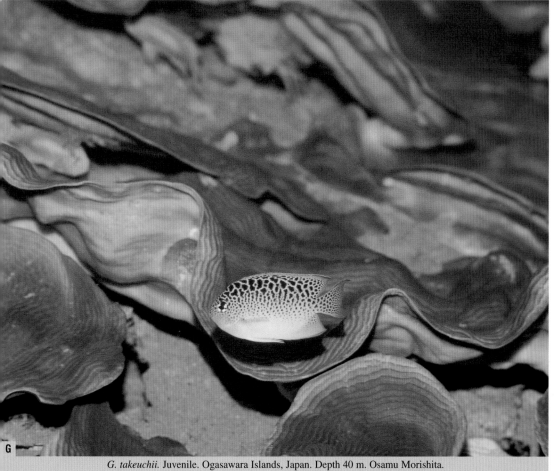

G

G. takeuchii. Juvenile. Ogasawara Islands, Japan. Depth 40 m. Osamu Morishita.

Genicanthus personatus Randall, 1975 Hawaii.

Restricted to the main and north-western Hawaiian Islands. Rarely seen in the main islands, where it prefers depths below 60 m, and it is more common in the north-western islands where it can be encountered as shallow as 27 m. Occurs in the cooler waters of seaward reef slopes or drop-offs. Both males and females immaculately white with contrasting bright markings on the head and median fins. Females have black above the mouth, ranging from a stripe above the lips to a large area reaching eyes, and below the mouth to the cheek spine, and a broad black band on tail, whilst males have an orange-yellow face and orange on outer halves of dorsal and anal fins. Juveniles have a dark head-band, running over the eye. Length to 21 cm.

Remarks: the Masked Angelfish was discovered in 1972, and remains one of divers favourite fishes. Only four specimens were known when described in 1975, all females. Just a few months later the first males were collected and the species was re-described the same year.

Aquarium: it is a very sensitive species to keep in home aquaria, especially large males, but only recently it spawned at the Waikiki Aquarium, and some young were raised successfully.

A   B

G. personatus. Females with different markings. **A** Pearl & Hermes reef, nw Hawaiian Is. Jim Watt, **B** Midway Atoll. Ed Robinson.

C

G. personatus. Male. Pearl & Hermes reef, north-western Hawaiian Islands. Jim Watt.

D *G. personatus.* Female with lots of black on head. Pearl & Hermes reef, north-western Hawaiian Islands. Jim Watt.

E *G. personatus.* Male on the left and a facing female on the right. Midway Atoll. Ed Robinson.

Feminine. Type species: *Holacanthus multifasciatus* Smith & Radcliffe, 1911. Comprising 3 species, 2 of which were, until recently, included with *Centropyge*, and a third discovered more recently. Their distribution is 2 species in the West Pacific and 1 in the south Pacific. They are similar in appearance to that genus, but are deeper bodied and have a different style of colour patterns. All remain small, rarely reaching 10 cm. Young are very similar to adults, except *Paracentropyge multifasciata* which has an ocellus on soft dorsal fin in small juveniles, and none show sexual dimorphism. Their diet is not well known, but some reports suggest that they feed on benthic inverts. Adults are often observed dwelling upside down in somewhat darker places such as caves or large overhangs of reefs and most live at depths well over 20 m. *P. boylei* lives very deep and has only been accessible to divers using mixed gas diving equipment. All have proven to be shy in the aquarium and rather hard to acclimate. Hybrids between two of the species were collected in the wild, giving support to their separate status from *Centropyge*. Previous authors placed *P. venusta* in at least three other different generic names.

List of species. Genus *Paracentropyge*

1. *P. boylei*   *Paracentropyge boylei* Pyle & Randall, 1992. Roratonga, Cook Islands. (p. **167**)
2. *P. multifasciata*   *Holacanthus multifasciatus* Smith & Radcliffe, 1911. Philippines. (p. **164**)
3. *P. venusta*   *Holacanthus venusta* Yasuda & Tominaga, 1969. Oshima, Japan. (p. **162**)

picture index to *Paracentropyge* species

P. *venusta* **162**

P. multifasciata **164**

P. boylei **167**

Paracentropyge venusta. Iriomote, Japan.
Depth 25 m. Length 12 cm. Rudie Kuiter.

Holacanthus venusta Yasuda & Tominaga, 1969.
Oshima, Japan.

North-western Pacific, southern Japan, Taiwan, the Philippines and Palau. Found mainly on outer reef slopes or drop-offs to at least 40 m depth. Not so much on coral reefs and usually inhabits caves or holes of steep walls where it typically swims upside down, (most photographs from the wild are inverted here). Adults are mostly blue with yellow below, from snout to anal fin, and in the young, a yellow band extends behind the head. Fairly commonly seen in certain areas of the Tokaras, north of Amami-ohshima, Kagoshima Prefecture, and in the Izu Islands. In Palau it is rare. Seen solitary, in pairs and occasionally in small groups of up to three or four individuals. Length to 12 cm.

Remarks: was referred to the genus *Holacanthus* for a long time and later to *Centropyge*, and in 1991 to *Sumireyakko*. Hybrid forms with *Paracentropyge multifasciata* are offered in the aquarium trade at high prices.

Aquarium: a difficult species to keep in captivity for a long period, often due to starvation or because it suddenly dies for no apparent reason. However, some individuals do well. Most aquarium specimens available were around 7 cm and rarely smaller than 3 cm, but recent shipments from the Philippines to Japan included many juveniles of about 3 cm, suggesting that these must have been aquacultured. Such fish may be easier to keep.

P. venusta. Iriomote, Japan. Depth 25 m. Length 12 cm. Rudie Kuiter.

P. venusta. Typically upside-down against the ceiling of a cave. Iriomote, Japan. Depth 25 m. Length 12 cm. Rudie Kuiter.

D

P. venusta. Juvenile, aquarium, Japan. Hiroyuki Tanaka.

E

P. venusta. Pair in aquarium, Germany. Helmut Debelius.

F

G

P. venusta. **G** is inverted. Iriomote, Japan. Depth 25 m. Length 12 cm. Rudie Kuiter.

Many-banded Angelfish *Paracentropyge multifasciata*

Holacanthus multifasciatus Smith & Radcliffe, 1911. Philippines.

Widespread Western Pacific, ranging from the Ryukyus, Japan, to the Great Barrier Reef, scattered localities in the South Pacific, Samoa and east to the Society Islands, straying to Easter Island, and also at Cocos-Keeling and Christmas Island in the eastern Indian Ocean. Inhabits crevices and caves on outer reef slopes or drop-offs at depths of 20 m or more. Seems to have a preference for large reef overhangs, especially where sponges grow from the ceilings and often swims upside down in such places. This species is readily identified by its distinctive colour pattern of alternating black and white bands, the black changing to yellow ventrally. Juveniles feature a reflective blue spot, edged with white anteriorly, on the end of the dorsal fin. Length to 12 cm.

Remarks: very rare in the Yaeyamas, Japan, the northern extent of its range, and becomes more common going south, and most common in Indonesia. Several apparent hybrids with *Paracentropyge venusta* were collected in the Philippines and shipped to Japan. The occurrence of hybrids between the two species made ichthyologists realise that they are closely related and belonged to the same genus.

Aquarium: a timid fish, often refuses any food offered in the aquarium at first. Some individuals can survive for a while, but it is rather difficult to keep them long in captivity.

P. multifasciata. Flores, Indonesia. Depth 20–30 m. **A** length 20 mm. **B** length 45 mm. Rudie Kuiter.

P. multifasciata. Flores, Indonesia. Depth 25 m. Length 10 cm. Rudie Kuiter.

P. multifasciata. Flores, Indonesia. Depth 30 m. Length 10 cm. Rudie Kuiter.

P. multifasciata. Flores, Indonesia. Depth 25 m. Length 12 cm. Rudie Kuiter.

A *P. venusta.* Aquarium, Japan. **B** *P. multifasciata.* Flores, Indonesia. Depth 25 m. Length 10 cm. Rudie Kuiter.

P. multifasciata ✕ *venusta.* Aquarium. Hybrid from the Philippines. Parent species above. Helmut Debelius.

Candy-striped Angelfish
Paracentropyge boylei

Centropyge boylei Pyle & Randall, 1992.
Rarotonga, Cook Islands, South Pacific.

Only known from the type locality. Inhabits coral rubble on steep outer reefs at depths of 52–115 m. Easily identified by the pattern of bright orange vertical bands. Juvenile stages have fewer bands compared with the adults. The largest recorded specimen is 7 cm but it probably grows larger.

Remarks: a remarkable discovery made by deep diving using mixed gas. First seen in 1989 by a collector at 93 m, who later took an ichthyologist down with him to 112 metres to search for this strikingly marked angelfish. They were successful in collecting three specimens as well as two of *Centropyge narcosis*. The most shallow *Paracentropyge boylei* observed was at 52 m but generally specimens were seen in excess of 70 m.

Aquarium: a shy and very difficult species to keep. Someone who started to feed it with 'live' rocks was successful. Some three years have passed since he started it. Very few are collected and most are shipped to Japan, but it demands as high a price as a new Japanese car. First imported to Japan in 1991, together with *Centropyge narcosis*.

A

P. boylei. Aquarium. Length about 6 cm. Atsushi Morioka.

B

C

P. boylei. Aquarium. **B** length about 5 cm. Yutaka Niino. **C** length about 4 cm. Richard Pyle.

Feminine. Type species: *Holacanthus tibicen* Cuvier, 1831. A large genus with at least 32 members, but dividable into several distinct groups or subgenera. They are commonly referred to as pygmy angelfishes, due to their generally much smaller size than other angelfish genera. The species are variably distributed in tropical and subtropical seas of the world. Few have large geographical distributions and some are endemic to tiny oceanic outposts, an island, or small island group. They occur on algal-rocky and coral reefs, and most species live in shallow waters at depths to about 15 m, but some range to 70 m or more, and a few inhabit only depths of more than 50 m. Pygmy angelfishes are quick-darting and often shy species that hug the substrates with tunnels and crevices, ready to disappear and appear again several metres away. Many of the shallow water species feed exclusively on algae and detritus, however, some vary their diet with small crustaceans or other invertebrates, especially in deeper water.

List of species. Genus ***Centropyge***

1.	*C. acanthops*	*Holacanthus acanthops* Norman, 1922. Durban, South Africa. (p. 200)
2.	*C. argi*	*Centropyge argi* Woods & Kanazawa, 1951. Bermuda Island. (p. 202)
3.	*C. aurantia*	*Centropyge aurantius* Randall & Wass, 1974. Solomon Islands. (p. 185)
4.	*C. aurantonotus*	*Centropyge aurantonotus* Burgess, 1974. Barbados, West Indies. (p. 203)
5.	*C. bicolor*	*Chaetodon bicolor* Bloch, 1787. East Indies. (p. 176)
6.	*C. bispinosa*	*Holacanthus bispinosus* Günther, 1860. Vanuatu. (p. 186)
7.	*C. colini*	*Centropyge colini* Smith-Vaniz & Randall, 1974. Cocos-Keeling. (p. 205)
8.	*C. debelius*	*Centropyge debelius* Pyle, 1990. Mauritius. (p. 196)
9.	*C. eibli*	*Centropyge eibli* Klausewitz, 1963. Nicobar Islands. (p. 182)
10.	*C. ferrugata*	*Centropyge ferrugatus* Randall & Burgess, 1972. Ishigaki, Japan. (p. 190)
11.	*C. fisheri*	*Holacanthus fisheri* Snyder, 1904. Oahu I, Hawaii. (p. 199)
12.	*C. flavicauda*	*Centropyge flavicauda* Fraser-Brunner, 1933. South China Sea. (p. 198)
13.	*C. flavipectoralis*	*Centropyge flavipectoralis* Randall & Klausewitz, 1977. Sri Lanka. (p. 184)
14.	*C. flavissima*	*Holacanthus. flavissimus* Cuvier, 1831. Caroline Island. (p. 178)
15.	*C. heraldi*	*Centropyge heraldi* Woods & Shultz, 1953. Marshall Islands. (p. 174)
16.	*C. hotumatua*	*Centropyge hotumatua* Randall & Caldwell, 1973. Easter Island. (p. 198)
17.	*C. interrupta*	*Angelichthys interruptus* Tanaka, 1918. Tanabe, Japan. (p. 192)
18.	*C. joculator*	*Centropyge joculator* Smith-Vaniz & Randall, 1974. Cocos-Keeling. (p. 197)
19.	*C. loriculus*	*Holacanthus loriculus* Günther, 1874. Society Islands. (p. 188)
20.	*C. multicolor*	*Centropyge multicolor* Randall & Wass, 1974. Marshall Islands. (p. 194)
21.	*C. multispinis*	*Centropyge multispinis* Playfair & Günther, 1867. (p. 183)
22.	*C. nahackyi*	*Centropyge nahackyi* Kosaki, 1989. Johnson Island. (p. 195)
23.	*C. narcosis*	*Centropyge narcosis* Pyle & Randall, 1992. Cook Islands. (p. 204)
24.	*C. nigriocellus*	*Centropyge nigriocellus* Woods & Schultz, 1953. Johnson Island. (p. 204)
25.	*C. nox*	*Holacanthus nox* Bleeker, 1853. Ambon. (p. 173)
26.	*C. potteri*	*Holacanthus potteri* Jordan & Metz, 1912. Oahu I, Hawaii. (p. 191)
27.	*C. resplendens*	*Centropyge resplendens* Lubbock & Sankey, 1975. (p. 203)
28.	*C. shepardi*	*Centropyge shepardi* Randall & Yasuda, 1979. Guam. (p. 189)
29.	*C. tibicen*	*Holacanthus tibicen* Cuvier, 1831. No locality. (p. 172)
30.	*C. vrolikii*	*Holacanthus vrolikii* Bleeker, 1853. Ambon. (p. 180)
31.	*C. cf vrolikii*	*Centropyge cf vrolikii*. Undescribed species. Rowley Shoals. (p. 181)
32.	*C. woodheadi*	*Centropyge. woodheadi* Kuiter, 1998. Fiji. (p. 175)

Adults often pair or live in a harem-like group, depending on the species, and how common they are, and sometimes this varies between different areas. There is no obvious colour difference between the sexes, but sometimes males may have more pointed fins than females. Juveniles are very similar in colour to their adults, usually with bolder markings, and some juveniles feature an ocellus on the body or dorsal fin. When maturing they first become females and some individuals change sex, usually determined by the circumstances, such as when pairing or living in groups in a harem-like arrangement. Normally the largest becomes male, and in a group the next largest female is in line to change if the male drops out. In some species males have reverted back to females. In general they are excellent aquarium fishes as they are small, many less than 10 cm long, and usually very attractive. As they exhibit interesting behaviour as well, it is not surprising that they are amongst the most popular fishes with aquarists. Most species are easily kept and will accept all kinds of food, given that water conditions are good and they are provided with some small caves or swim-throughs. A few species, and sometimes certain individuals, may have trouble acclimatising due to them needing a more specific diet or being poorly treated during collecting or transport. More and more species are being aquacultured and of course these individuals are much more suitable for the home aquarium.

Model *Centropyge eibli*, aquarium (Helmut Debelius) and its mimic *Acanthurus tristis*, Bali, Indonesia (Rudie Kuiter).

In the Indo-Pacific a number of *Centropyge* species serve as models to two species of surgeonfishes, the Indian Mimic Surgeon *Acanthurus tristis* and the Pacific Mimic Surgeon *A. pyroferus* (for detail see 'Surgeonfishes, Rabbitfishes and their Relatives' from this Marine Fish Families Series). The juveniles of these are perfect copies of some of the pygmy angelfishes, depending on their localities. *A. tristis* mimics *Centropyge eibli*, whilst *A. pyroferus* mimics several species: *C. flavissima*, *C. heraldi*, *C. vrolikii*, and one known case *C. bicolor*. Only when looking closely is it possible to distinguish the mimic from the model by the differences in the shape of the mouth. Looking just like the pygmy angelfish gives the juvenile surgeons some protection from predators which have learned that angelfishes are too difficult to capture. The angelfish settle as postlarvae at a very small size whilst the surgeonfishes are much larger when settling. By the time a postlarval angelfish has reached the size of the settling surgeonfish stage, it has learned to avoid predators and swims more openly about. The surgeonfish juvenile needs to feed on algae that grows best in the more open and exposed areas and becomes less of a target by looking like the experienced quick and clever little angelfish.

Centropyge loriculus. Cook Islands, South Pacific. Depth 15 m. Where common, pygmies are often moving about in small groups that live in Harem-style, with one male looking after all the females. Helmut Debelius.

picture index to *Centropyge* species

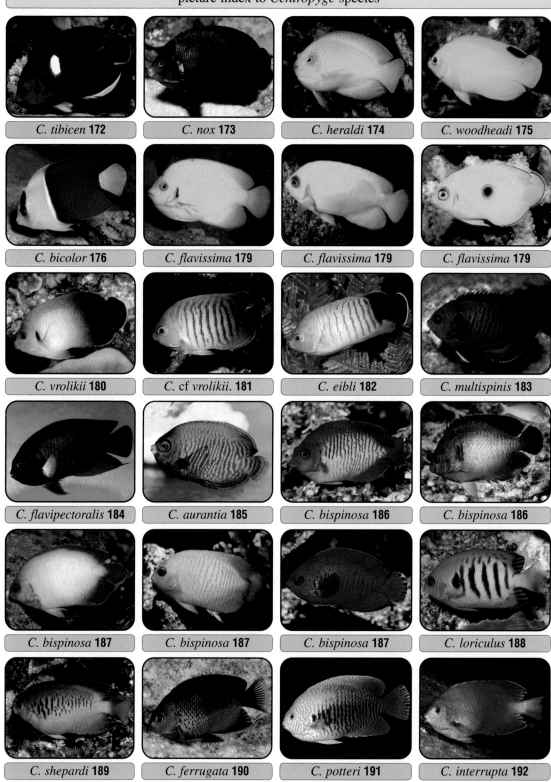

C. tibicen **172**	*C. nox* **173**	*C. heraldi* **174**	*C. woodheadi* **175**
C. bicolor **176**	*C. flavissima* **179**	*C. flavissima* **179**	*C. flavissima* **179**
C. vrolikii **180**	*C. cf vrolikii.* **181**	*C. eibli* **182**	*C. multispinis* **183**
C. flavipectoralis **184**	*C. aurantia* **185**	*C. bispinosa* **186**	*C. bispinosa* **186**
C. bispinosa **187**	*C. bispinosa* **187**	*C. bispinosa* **187**	*C. loriculus* **188**
C. shepardi **189**	*C. ferrugata* **190**	*C. potteri* **191**	*C. interrupta* **192**

C. multicolor 194

C. nahackyi 195

C. debelius 196

C. joculator 197

C. hotumatua 198

C. flavicauda 198

C. fisheri 199

C. acanthops 200

C. argi 202

C. aurantonotus 203

C. resplendens 203

C. narcosis 204

C. nigriocellus 204

C. colini 205

A

Keyhole Angelfish *Centropyge tibicen*

Holacanthus tibicen Cuvier,1831. No locality.

Widespread tropical Western Pacific, from Japan to Australia, ranging west to Thailand, Christmas Island and Western Australia and east to Coral Sea and New South Wales. Expatriates south to Montague Island and coastal waters of southern New South Wales. Often a common species found in various habitats from silty coastal bays and harbours to outer reefs. Adults occur in small loose groups where common. Small juveniles secretive in narrow crevices, often where sea-urchins rest during the day. Adults and juveniles are readily identified by their mostly black colour and a conspicuous white vertical bar or blotch centrally on the body. In tiny juveniles it is usually present as a narrow bar from top to bottom, shortening and widening proportionally with growth. First a yellow border on the anal fin develops with growth and then a narrow blue line between the black and yellow, that lines up with the blue margins of the caudal and dorsal fins appears. Some large individuals are black with a blue hue, probably males. Length to 15 cm.

Remarks: reported to 18 cm long, but this seems to be greatly exaggerated, usually to 12 cm.

Aquarium: one of the easiest of the pygmy angels to keep. Grows quickly when juvenile and feeds on a variety of foods, including unwelcome algae growth in an aquarium.

B

C. tibicen. Sulawesi, Indonesia. D 5 m. L. 14 cm. Rudie Kuiter.

C

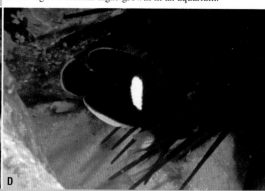

D

C. tibicen. Sydney region, eastern Australia. **C** aquarium grown 45 mm. **D** Seal Rocks. D. 6 m. L. 30 mm. Rudie Kuiter.

E

F

C. tibicen. Bali, Indonesia. **E** depth 15 m. Length 10 cm. **F** depth 6 m. Length 75 mm. Rudie Kuiter.

Midnight Angelfish *Centropyge nox*

Holacanthus nox Bleeker, 1853. Ambon.

Widespread throughout the Western Pacific, ranging from southern Japan and Micronesia to northern Australia and Coral Sea. Occurs from coastal reef slopes to steep outer reef walls in sessile invertebrate habitats mixed with algae. Often in large caves but may venture out on rubble seabeds with coralline algae growth in small loose groups. Quickly retreats to cover when approached. Occurs at depths to at least 70 m, but more common at the 20 m level, rarely shallower. Readily identified by its almost completely black colour, and in large adults it has a yellowish blotch behind the end of the gill cover. This angelfish remains near its shelter and quickly retires to the crevices when threatened. A rather shy and secretive species. Length to 9 cm.

Remarks: the midnight dottyback *Pseudochromis paranox* is thought to be a mimic of *Centropyge nox* and these two have been seen together in some areas, but just being black may be coincidental. Dottybacks and pygmy angelfishes share similar habitats and behaviour, both are clever in avoiding predators and there appears to be no reason for a case of mimicry.

Aquarium: many aquarists experienced problems keeping this species, but on the other hand others have kept this species for long periods. This may be a reflection of the condition of specimens when purchased.

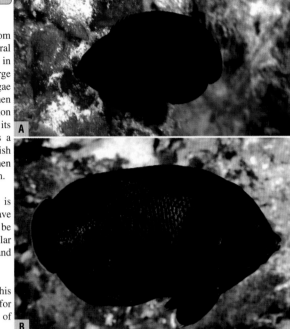

C. nox. Flores, Indonesia. D 25 m. L. 40 & 85 mm. Rudie Kuiter.

C. nox. C aquarium. Xanthic, from Flores, Indonesia. Yutaka Niino. D aquarium, Australia. Length 9 cm. Rudie Kuiter.

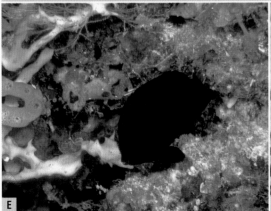

C. nox. Indonesia. E Flores depth 35 m. Length 8 cm. F Bali. Depth 12 m. Length 10 cm. Rudie Kuiter.

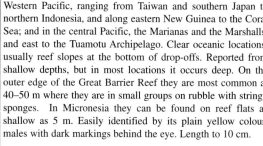

Herald's Angelfish *Centropyge heraldi*

Centropyge heraldi Woods & Schultz, 1953. Marshall Islands.

Western Pacific, ranging from Taiwan and southern Japan to northern Indonesia, and along eastern New Guinea to the Coral Sea; and in the central Pacific, the Marianas and the Marshalls, and east to the Tuamotu Archipelago. Clear oceanic locations, usually reef slopes or the bottom of drop-offs. Reported from shallow depths, but in most locations it occurs deep. On the outer edge of the Great Barrier Reef they are most common at 40–50 m where they are in small groups on rubble with stringy sponges. In Micronesia they can be found on reef flats as shallow as 5 m. Easily identified by its plain yellow colour, males with dark markings behind the eye. Length to 10 cm.

Remarks: sometimes the mimic surgeonfish, *Acanthurus pyroferus* is mistaken for this species.

C. heraldi. Kerama, Japan. D. 25 m. L. 10 cm. Rudie Kuiter.

Aquarium: this species is normally hardy and can be kept in an invertebrates aquarium, but sometimes it dies unexpectedly for no apparent reason.

C. heraldi. Eastern Field, nw Coral Sea Bob Halstead.

C. heraldi. **D** Cook Is, South Pacific. Malcolm Francis. **E** Sulawesi, Indonesia. Depth 20 m. Length 50 mm. Rudie Kuiter.

C. heraldi. Kerama, Japan. Depth 25 m. Length 10 cm. Rudie Kuiter.

Woodhead's Angelfish *Centropyge woodheadi*

Centropyge woodheadi Kuiter, 1998. Fiji.

Coral Sea, from Gulf of Papua and Solomon Islands, and east to Samoa and Tonga. It occurs on open rubble and boulder habitats at depths of 9–20 m, but most common at about 12 m. Identified by the bright yellow colour overall and normally features a prominent elongate black streak along much of the soft dorsal fin, offset by an irridescent blue margin. The amount of black is variable and ranges from a spot at the end to the entire length of the soft dorsal fin. In the Solomon Islands some large males were observed that featured a very extensive large black area and a more orange head. Length to at least 12 cm.

Remarks: prior to description this species was thought to be a geographical variation of the more widespread *Centropyge heraldi*, but they are sympatric, at least in the north-western part of the Coral Sea. *C. woodheadi* grows slightly larger and

A

C. woodheadi. Vanuatu. Length 10 cm. Malcolm Francis.

prefers shallower habitats. The black dorsal spot that usually characterises this species varies greatly in size and may fade in captivity, but *C. heraldi* never develops such a spot.

Aquarium: reputed to be easily kept in captivity.

B

C. woodheadi. Eastern Field, nw Coral Sea. Bob Halstead.

C D

C. woodheadi. **C** Holmes Reef, Coral Sea. D. 20 m. L. 8 cm. Phil Woodhead. **D** Tuvalu, South Pacific. D. 17 m. Helmut Debelius.

E

C. woodheadi. Vanuatu. Together with yellow bristletooth surgeonfishes *Ctenochaetus flavicauda*. Malcolm Francis.

Chaetodon bicolor Bloch, 1787. East Indies.

Widespread tropical Western Pacific, ranging from Japan to Australia, and Sumatra to Samoa. Expatriates to subtropical zones, transported by current during their pelagic stage. Common in most areas but becomes rarer in the western and eastern extremes. Usually found on rocky and coral reefs at depths between 10–25 m, but in some areas that are sheltered and have good water quality, it can be observed in just a few metres depth. Where common, the adults are nearly always in small groups that actively move about in gutters or amongst corals to feed on algae. Juveniles are solitary and secretive in crevices. A very distinctive species that is immediately recognised by its half yellow, half blue colouring and its blue band above the eyes. Length to 15 cm.

Remarks: sometimes exhibits strange colour patterns in the Coral Sea as shown on opposite page.

Aquarium: normally feeds on algae and a variety of small invertebrates. However, when obtained as an adult, it may pick on some corals and may refuse any food offered. Best to get small specimens or introduce them to a large aquarium.

C. bicolor. Bali, Indonesia. D 5 m. L. 8 & 14 cm. Rudie Kuiter.

C. bicolor. Captured in 5 m depth, Bermagui, southern New South Wales, eastern Australia. Representing its most southern record. **C** as captured, length just under 20 mm. **E** after a few weeks, and **D** several months later, about 45 mm. Rudie Kuiter.

F

C. bicolor. Adult group. Indonesia. Helmut Debelius.

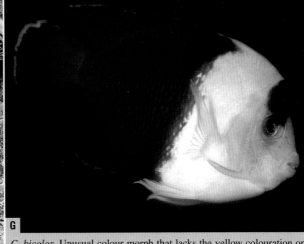

G

C. bicolor. Unusual colour morph that lacks the yellow colouration on the head and tail. Holmes Reef, Coral Sea. Depth 12 m. Length 7 cm. Fenton Walsh.

H

C. bicolor. Aquarium. **H** to **K** photographs taken of the same individual from Moore Reefs, Great Barrier Reef, off Cairn, Australia. Depth 5 m. Length 10 cm. Fenton Walsh.

The photographer and collector of this strange morph kept this individual for a considerable time. Amazingly it eventually changed to the normal colouration after about 7 weeks. He said that such morphs appear at a certain time of the year when spawning is at its peak, and perhaps the cause of the strange colouration. Similarly this happens in a few more *Centropyge* species in the Coral Sea (see *C. bispinosa*).

I

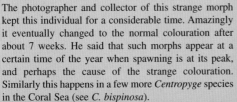

J

K

Lemonpeel Angelfish *Centropyge flavissima*
Holacanthus flavissimus Cuvier, 1831. Caroline Islands.

Ranges in the Western Pacific from southern Japan, Micronesia and Philippines to Coral Sea, central Pacific to the Marquesas and southeastern Indian Ocean, but not into Indonesia, except for Irian Jaya. Separate and different-looking population in Christmas Island, Cocos-Keeling and south coast of Java. In most areas this species is usually seen at a depth of about 20 m, sometimes at 25 m in coral rich areas, but in Guam it is a common species and often much shallower. Very distinctive species being bright yellow with iridescent blue lines highlighting the eyes, gills and fins. Juveniles feature a large blue-edged black ocellus centrally on the side. Reaches a size of 14 cm.

Remarks: hybridises with several congeners. Indian Ocean population differs in colour from Pacific one in lacking the blue ring around the eye and has a black edge on the posterior margin of the operculum. The juvenile feature of the ocellus on the side of the body, lost at small size, is retained until subadult size in the Indian Ocean population. It seems that these populations have been isolated for a long time and either represent subspecies or further research may prove them to be valid species.

Aquarium: can be kept in a reef set-up where it will probably leave invertebrates alone, but also does well in a fish community aquarium. Individuals may live for a long time, reported as long as 11 years in captivity, but some have died unexpectedly for no apparent reason, looking healthy and happy one day and seemingly having a stroke the next. Over feeding? This species is now aquacultured and is better for the home aquarium.

A

C. flavissima. Kumejima, Okinawa, Japan. Tsuyoshi Kawamoto.

B

C. flavissima. Guam, Micronesia. Depth 7 m Adult pair, length about 12 cm. Rudie Kuiter.

C. *flavissima*. **C** Juvenile in southern Japan. Hiroshi Takeuchi. **D** Guam, Micronesia. Depth 7 m, length 12 cm. Rudie Kuiter.

C. *flavissima*. Christmas Island, I.O. **E** subadult with ocellus. D. 12 m. Length 6 cm. **F** adult. D. 5 m. Length 14 cm. Jerry Allen.

hybrid *Centropyge flavissima* X sp morphs

Probable hybrids *C. flavissima* X *vrolikii*. **G** aquarium, Japan. Yutaka Niino. **H** Holmes Reef, Coral Sea. Fenton Walsh.

Hybrid *C. flavissima* X *eibli*. **I** Christmas Island, I.O. Jerry Allen. **J** juvenile, aquarium. Japan. Origin unknown. Yutaka Niino.

A

C. vrolikii. Sulawesi. D 9 m. L. 12 cm. Rudie Kuiter.

B

C. vrolikii. Bali, Indonesia. D 6 m. L. 9 cm. Rudie Kuiter.

C

D

C. vrolikii. Eastern Australia. **C** Byron Bay. D. 15 m. L. 6 cm. **D** Aquarium, Sydney specimen. D. 3 m. L. 18 mm. Rudie Kuiter.

Pearly-scaled Angelfish *Centropyge vrolikii*

Holacanthus vrolikii Bleeker, 1853. Ambon.

Widespread Western Pacific, from southern Japan to southern Indonesia and north-eastern Australia, ranging east to Micronesia and the Coral Sea. Replaced by *Centropygy eibli* from Java and Pacific eastern side of Sumatra. Juveniles expatriate to subtropical zones. A shallow water species in lagoons, coastal and seaward reefs to about 25 m depth. Mostly pearl grey and black posteriorly on body and unpaired fins. A black or orange bar on the operculum. Length to 12 cm.

Remarks: species name often misspelled "*vroliki*" or "*vrolicki*". Commonly hybridises in some areas: in the Marshalls, where uncommon, with the common *Centropyge flavissima*, and in Bali, where common, with the uncommon *C. eibli*. In some areas *C. vrolikii* sometimes shows a faint banded pattern, reminiscent of that of *C. eibli*. Juveniles in Flores often have this. A new species with distinct bands was found in the Rowley Shoals off north-western Australia, and interestingly a pipefish thought to be endemic to the Flores Sea was discovered at the Rowley Shoals at the same time, indicating a connection from the past. It appears that the Rowley Shoals population became isolated from the Pacific Fauna a long time ago and the strongly banded form evolved from a *vrolikii*-like ancestor, just as *eibli* did independently.

Aquarium: an easy species to keep in home aquariums and accepts most foods offered, including vegetable matter.

E

C. eibli ✕ vrolikii. Bali, Indonesia. Depth 10 m. Length 9. cm. In this area C. eibli is the least common. Rudie Kuiter.

F

C. vrolikii. Juvenile with vertical bars. Flores, Indonesia. Depth 6 m. Length 4 cm. See remarks. Rudie Kuiter.

Black Tiger Angelfish
Centropyge cf *vrolikii*
Undetermined species

The Rowley Shoals, off Western Australia only. Moderately common along the upper slopes near deep drop-offs in about 10–20 m depth. Most were seen in small groups in dense corals and were often seen grazing on rubble, but quickly darted for cover when approached. One of the shyest species encountered and difficult to photograph. It looks similar to *Centropyge eibli*, but posterior part of body is almost black, like that in *C. vrolikii*; and the vertical stripes are broad and dusky. The margin of the dorsal spines is orange. It is a small species, the largest specimens measuring about 8 cm, and no larger fish were observed in the wild.

A

Remarks: prior to 2001 it was recorded from the Rowley Shoals as *Centropyge eibli*, but it may be more closely related to *C. vrolikii*. The area of the Rowley Shoals is more like a Pacific outpost, despite its location in the eastern Indian Ocean. Species normally found in the Pacific occur there, such as *Siganus doliatus*, but show differences in colour. *Pseudanthias tuka*-males display with bright yellow dorsal fins, whilst *P. pleurotaenia*-males only turn on their normally permanent white square during display. It appears that the region became isolated from the Pacific a long time ago, and because of its remoteness and being an extensive region, it was able to sustain a fauna of its own. Clearly *C. vrolikii*, *C. eibli* and this apparently undescribed species share a common ancestor and separation may have happened at about the same time. Possibly their ancestor was striped and these were lost in *C. vrolikii*. The 'Black Tiger Angelfish' is now under investigation as a number of specimens were collected.

B

C

D

C. cf *vrolikii*. Rowley Shoals, WA, Australia. Lengths: **A** 6 cm. **B** 3 cm. **C** 5 cm. **D** 8 cm. Rudie Kuiter.

E

C. cf *vrolikii*. Rowley Shoals, WA, Australia. Depth 20 m. Length 7 cm. Rudie Kuiter.

A

C. eibli. Bali, Indonesia. D 5 m. L. 9 cm. Rudie Kuiter.

B

C. eibli. Christmas I., I.O. D. 15 m. L. 10 cm. Jerry Allen.

C

C. eibli. Bali, Indonesia. D 15 m. L. 8 cm. Rudie Kuiter.

E

Eibl's Angelfish *Centropyge eibli*

Centropyge eibli Klausewitz, 1963. Nicobar Islands.

Eastern Indian Ocean, ranging from the Maldives and Andaman Sea to Indonesia, east to Bali where uncommon and greatly outnumbered by its closest relative *Centropyge vrolikii*. Usually seen in coral rich areas in coastal and inner reef areas, from silty to pristine habitats, and from shallow reef slopes to about 25 m depth. Identified by its pale body with thin vertical orange lines and black tail. Length to 11 cm.

Remarks: named after Irenäus Eibl-Eibesfeldt, a famous German authority on animal behaviour who wrote the classic 'Land of a Thousand Atolls' about his voyage during which he discovered this species. *Centropyge eibli* is known to hybridise with other related species like *C. vrolikii* or *C. flavissima*. At Christmas Island, where this species is common, a cross with the less common *C. flavissima* was photographed, and hybrids with *C. vrolikii* are well known, especially in the eastern part of Indonesia (Bali), where this species is uncommon.

Aquarium: a popular species among aquarists, best kept in community fish tanks; it may nip some invertebrates. A fairly hardy species for the home aquarium.

D

C. eibli. Bali, Indonesia. D 12 m. L. 35 mm. Rudie Kuiter.

F

C. eibli. Java, Indonesia.. Depth. 5 m. **E** length 11 cm. **F** gravid female. Length 75 mm. Rudie Kuiter.

Many-spined Angelfish *Centropyge multispinis*

Holacanthus multispinis Playfair, 1867. Zanzibar.

Indian Ocean, ranging from the Red Sea and east coasts of Africa to the Maldives and to Andaman Sea, just reaching Sumatra. It inhabits rubble bottoms and coral rich areas to a depth of about 30 m. Found also in rocky tide pools in South Africa. In the wild this fish looks almost black. It has an overall dark bluish-brown colour with indistinct vertical barring on the body. The only conspicuous markings are a dark ocellus at eye-level above the pectoral-fin base and the blue margins on the ventral and anal fins. Some blue reflective bands show up in the median fins when seen from certain angles. Length to 13 cm.

Remarks: named for the numerous spines on its cheek, but also known as Dusky Cherub in South Africa. Easily confused with *Centropyge flavipectoralis*. The two species are sympatric in the Maldives and Andaman Sea. Both are generally dark in their appearance, but markings are quite different and only *C. flavipectoralis* has yellowish pectoral fins.

Aquarium: easily kept in captivity and can live a long time when cared for and provided with lots of hiding places like most pygmy angels enjoy, often behaving in a playful way.

A

C. multispinis. Red Sea. D. 10 m. L. 7 cm. Rudie Kuiter.

B

C

C. multispinis. **B** aquarium From Sri Lanka. Length 9 cm. **C** Red Sea. Depth 10 m. Length 5 cm. Rudie Kuiter.

D

E

C. multispinis. **D** Maldives. Helmut Debelius. **E** Sodwana Bay, South Africa. Depth 16 m. Length 12 cm. Rudie Kuiter.

A

C. flavipectoralis. Maldives. Depth 25 m. Length 10 cm. Rudie Kuiter.

Yellowfin Angelfish *Centropyge flavipectoralis*

Centropyge flavipectoralis Randall & Klausewitz, 1977. Sri Lanka.

Eastern Indian Ocean, mainly in the Andaman Sea, ranging to the Maldives and northern Sumatra. In Sri Lanka it occurs on shallow rubble areas and reef edges to a depth of about 20 m, but in the Maldives the depth range is 20–40 m, where on rubble with sessile invertebrates. A dark looking species with a metallic blue shiny pattern of vertical bars on the body and anal fin, pale yellow pectoral fins, and thin blue margins on the median fins. Length to 10 cm.

Remarks: this species was first collected in 1955 and long regarded as a variation of *Centropyge multispinis*. Distinguished from that species in having yellow pectoral fins, and by the shiny blue pattern on its body.

Aquarium: a somewhat delicate species in captivity and needs to be kept with other fishes of similar size or smaller and should not have to compete too much for food. Few fish in all is best and providing lots of hiding places is recommended. Specimens from Sri Lanka are likely to be easiest to keep as these come from shallower water and also from less pristine conditions, and are therefore more tolerant.

C

B

C. flavipectoralis. Maldives. D. 25 m. L. 10 cm.
Showing its yellow pectoral fins. Rudie Kuiter.

D

E

C. flavipectoralis. **C–E** Singapore Under Water World Aquarium, Sri Lankan specimen. Rudie Kuiter.

Golden Angelfish *Centropyge aurantia*

Centropyge aurantius Randall & Wass, 1974.
American Samoa

Widespread, but known from scattered localities in the Pacific: Samoa, PNG & Solomons, northern GBR, Indonesia, Palau and Pohnpei. A secretive species, rarely seen by divers. Normally found in deep gutters amongst corals or crevices, and has been reported to 60 m depth, and in PNG as shallow as 3 m. Colour somewhat variable, usually dusky orange overall with numerous vertical narrow stripes on side. Some individuals are totally dark brown and may turn to orange, the more normal colouration, when kept in captivity for a while. Length to 10 cm, but usually much smaller: 5–6 cm.

Remarks: often shipped from Bali as Engel Melah (meaning: angel black).

Aquarium: a rather timid species, more suited to reef aquariums than fish only tanks, but it may nibble on some species of hard corals.

A

C. aurantia. Aquarium. From Lizard Island, GBR. L. 10 cm. Rudie Kuiter.

B

C. aurantia. Aquarium. Thought to be from Samoa. L. 6 cm. Richard Pyle.

C

D

C. aurantia. Aquarium. Specimens from Indonesia.
C Fenton Walsh. D Hiroyuki Tanaka.

E

C. aurantia. Sulawesi, Indonesia. D 6 m. L. 65 mm. Roger Steene.

C. bispinosa. Aquarium. G.B.R., Australia. Length 7 cm. Rudie Kuiter.

Coral Beauty *Centropyge bispinosa*

Holacanthus bispinosus Günther, 1860. Vanuatu.

The most widespread species in the Indo-West Pacific, ranging from East Africa through Indian Ocean islands and to the central Pacific Ocean to the Tuamotu Archipelago. Juveniles can be found in subtropical zones as expatriates. Occurs in a great variety of habitats from shallow rocky-algae to rich coral reefs and outer reef slopes to depths of at least 45 metres, depending on its geographical location. Extremely variable in colouration, although certain forms are habitat or depth related, or have a limited geographical distribution. The differences between some forms is so great that they look like completely different species. Most common form is dark blue with reddish vertical bars on the body and dark blue fins. Sometimes brilliantly blue all over, or even orange-red and patterned like *Centropyge aurantia*. In deep water they are often pale. The colouration of some morphs may change into the common form after a short time in captivity. Length to 10 cm.

Remarks: a hybrid *Centropyge bispinosa* **X** *shepardi* was reported from Guam.

Aquarium: easily kept in captivity and can live for a long time (about 10 years).

C. bispinosa. Deep-water form. GBR. D. 45 m. L. 10 cm. Rudie Kuiter.

C. bispinosa. **C** Flores, Indonesia. D. 10 m. L. 8 cm. **D** Aquarium, Sydney specimen. D. 4 m. L. 20 mm. Rudie Kuiter.

C. bispinosa. **E** Derawan, Malaysia. D. 15 m. L. 8 cm. **F** Flores, Indonesia. D. 20 m. L. 8 cm. Rudie Kuiter.

G

C. bispinosa. Sulawesi, Indonesia. Depth 15 m. Length 9 cm. Rudie Kuiter.

H

I

C. bispinosa. Juvenile blue morphs. **H** Moreton Bay, Qld, Australia. **I** Sulawesi, Indonesia. Rudie Kuiter.

J

K

C. bispinosa. Pale morph, Pacific. Length 7 cm. Jerry Allen.   *C. bispinosa*. Samoan variation, from 30 m. Fenton Walsh.

L

M

C. bispinosa. Variations from Holmes Reef, kept in aquarium and changed to normal colouration. Fenton Walsh.

Holacanthus loriculus Günther, 1874. Society Islands.

West to central Pacific, ranging from eastern Indonesia to the Marquesas Islands. Common in Palau, the Marianas, Marshalls and Society Islands. Depending on locality, occurs from shallow reef crest to 60 m. Readily identified by the bright orange to red colouration. Normally has several black bars on the body, but this varies geographically. Those in the Marquesas tend to possess a few or no bars, except the first black blotch behind gill cover. Hawaiian, Christmas and Line Islands individuals are often bright red. Length to 10 cm, but usually to 7 cm.

Remarks: this species is being aquacultured successfully in Hawaii. Massive exports are made from there and Majuro, the Marshalls.

Aquarium: a very popular species, especially red morphs, that easily adapt to captivity. As it does not harm inverts it is a great asset to the reef aquarium, but may give some species of ornamental shrimps a hard time.

A

C. loriculus. Big Island, Hawaii. Depth 11 m. Helmut Debelius.

B   C

C. loriculus. **B** Vanuatu. D. 6 m. L. 5 cm. Fenton Walsh. **C** aquarium. Coral Sea specimen. Rudie Kuiter.

D   E

C. loriculus. South Pacific localised morphs. **D** Marquesas. Peter Kragh. **E** Tuvalu. Helmut Debelius.

Shepard's Angelfish *Centropyge shepardi*

Centropyge shepardi Randall & Yasuda, 1979. Guam.

Northwestern Pacific (the Marianas, Bonins and recently photographed in Hachijoh-jima Island, the Izu Islands). Occurs in outer reef habitats from shallow lagoons to a depth of about 56 m. Colour mainly orange to orange-yellow with dark unpaired fins and narrower, short vertical bars on side. The bars are fewer in number in juvenile stages. Often with a dark blotch behind upper gill cover. Length to 12 cm.

Remarks: very similar to some certain colour forms of *Centropyge bispinosa* , and hybrids between these two have been reported from Guam. It is often available in aquarium shops in Guam. Hybrids between *C. shepardi* and another less similar species, *C. loriculus* were reported from Guam and other Micronesian waters.

Aquarium: easily adapts to captive environments and is suited to reef tanks as well. Smaller specimens are active and can quickly dart into crevices and it is best to give them plenty of hiding places just like other members of the genus.

A *C. shepardi*. Guam. D 20 m. L. 10 cm. Rudie Kuiter.

B *C. shepardi*. Ogasawara, Japan. Yasuhiro Morita.

C *C. shepardi*. Guam. **C** Unusual plain colour morph. Female. L. 7 cm. Robert Myers. **D** length 12 cm. Jerry Allen.

E *C. shepardi*. Habitat, comprising algae, sponges and corals. Guam. Depth 20 m. Length 10 cm. Rudie Kuiter.

A

B

Rusty Angelfish *Centropyge ferrugata*

Centropyge ferrugatus Randall & Burgess, 1972.
Ishigaki, Japan.

North-western Pacific Ocean, southern Japan including the Izu Islands to the Philippines and reported from Palau. Lives on rocky reefs and rubble areas at depths of about 6–30 m. Variable in colour from brick red on lower side and darker on upper half to a more creamy hue, and head slightly darker. Reaches a size of 10 cm.

Remarks: similar to *Centropyge shepardi* but it can be distinguished by the dark bars on its body, while *C. ferrugata* possesses numerous dark fine spots scattered over body. Commonly seen in Okinawa but rare in Palau (occurrence there needs to be confirmed).

D

C

F

E

C. ferrugata. Variations. Kerama, Japan. Depth 6 m. Lengths about 65 to 75 mm. Rudie Kuiter.

C. ferrugata. Spawning behaviour observed and photographed by **Yoji Ohkata** at Amami Oshima, Japan. Here, they spawn from start of summer until Autumn, during which water temperature is about 24–25°C. **D** rising from the bottom and the male nudging the female to encourage spawning. **F** gametes are released and can be seen as a small cloud left behind on return to the seabed. This behaviour is typical for most pygmies.

Potter's Angelfish *Centropyge potteri*

Holacanthus potteri Jordan & Metz, 1912. Hawaiian Is.

Only known from the Hawaiian Islands, Midway and Johnston Atoll. Adults inhabit shallow rocky, rubble and coral substrates, usually at depths over 10 m, but author H.T. saw one together with *Centropyge loriculus* in only 1 m when snorkeling in a harbour. An impressive sight. Juveniles are mostly shallow. Colour mainly orange to deep yellow with blue vertical bars overall. The amount of the orange/yellow may vary individually. Some specimens have dark broad bands on centre of body, while some are reddish pink with dark bars. Length to 10 cm.

Remarks: adults stay close to coral heads or rubble and are difficult to collect in the wild, while juveniles on rocky reefs are easier. Two specimens caught in deep waters (over 60 m) were predominantly blue with black-blue bars on side.

A

C. potteri. Oahu, Hawaiian Is. Length 10 cm. Robert Myers.

B

C. potteri. Midway Atoll. Jim Watt.

C

C. potteri. Hawaiian Islands. Length 10 cm. Jan Post.

D

E

C. potteri. Hawaiian Islands. **D** juvenile ~5 cm. Jerry Allen. **E** blue morph from 60+ m depth. L. 10 cm. Hiroyuki Tanaka.

Angelichthys interruptus Tanaka, 1918. Wakayama Pref., Japan.

Northern Pacific, ranging from southern Japan to Midway and the Hawaiian Islands. Inhabits rocky reefs and coral reefs to depths of about 60 m, usually deeper than 15 m. This species usually forms a harem, comprising the dominant male with several females or subadults (Shoichi Katoh, pers.comm.). Variable in colouration but basic colours bluish purple with orange or yellow. Males have an almost blue head, with spots around eye, which is yellowish in females. Some individuals in Midway population are more yellowish. In Hachijoh-jima yellow forms can be seen only in deeper water, while normal ones occur in shallower water. They are often observed taking faeces released from other fishes there. Perhaps the largest species in the genus, reaching up to 19 cm.

C. interrupta. Kashiwajima, Japan. Depth 25 m. Lengths: **A** ~15 cm. **B** ~17 cm. **C** ~14 cm. Rudie Kuiter.

C. interrupta. Small gathering of adults. Ogasawara Islands, Japan. Hiroshi Takeuchi.

Remarks: was long regarded as endemic to Japan, but now known to be fairly common in Midway Atoll. It is common in the Izu and Ogasawara Islands and often seen in certain areas of southern Honshu, Japan, but extremely rare in Okinawa.

Aquarium: often kept in living reef aquarium, but it may nibble on some species of hard corals.

C. interrupta. Ogasawara Islands, Japan. **E** small juvenile. **F** large adult. Hiroshi Takeuchi.

C. interrupta. Juveniles. **G** Izu Oceanic Park, Japan. D. 35 m. L. 35 mm. Rudie Kuiter. **H** Hachijoh Island. Tomoyo Mizutani.

C. interrupta. Pearl & Hermes reef, north-western Hawaiian Islands. Jim Watt.

Many-colour Pygmy Angelfish
Centropyge multicolor

Centropyge multicolor Randall & Wass, 1974. Marshall Is

Central Pacific, known from Marshalls, Marianas, Palau Society Islands, Fiji, and Cook & Hawaiian Islands Prefers areas of steep outer reef slopes at depths of 20–115 m. Colouring is a mix of yellow, blue and white and it has distinctive black and blue markings behind the eye. similar to *Centropyge nahackyi*, but has a pale upper body. Length to 9 cm, but usually less than 7 cm.

Remarks: one of a species complex that includes *Centropyge debelius* and *C. nahackyi*, each of which has only a limited distribution.

Aquarium: It can be easily kept for a long while in inver aquaria and fish tanks as well. This species is being aquacultured in Hawaii.

A

C. multicolor. Palau. D. 40 m. L. 8 cm. Hiroshi Nagano.

B

C. multicolor. Pair in typical habitat. Cook Islands. Depth 40 m. Length 8 cm. Helmut Debelius.

Nahacky's Pygmy Angelfish
Centropyge nahackyi

Centropyge nahackyi Kosaki, 1989. Johnston Atoll.

Limited to Johnston Atoll & Hawaiian Islands*. It occurs in a depth range of 25–70 m on reef slopes and rubble substrates. Body dark blue with lower anterior half yellow and also a yellow area posteriorly. Caudal fin bright yellow. A conspicuous head pattern with blue and black lines is the most distinctive feature. The back is dark which distinguishes it from the closest relative *Centropyge multicolor*. Length to 9 cm.

Remarks: *only one specimen was recorded from Kona Coast, Hawaiian Island.

Aquarium: rarely seen in the aquarium trade, but apparently it does well in captivity.

A

C. nahackyi. Johnston Atoll. Length 7 cm. Randall Kosaki.

B

C

C. nahackyi. Aquarium. Specimen from Johnston Atoll. Length 7 cm. Randall Kosaki.

D

C. nahackyi. Johnston Atoll. Depth 60 m. Randall Kosaki.

Blue Mauritius Angelfish *Centropyge debelius*

Centropyge debelius Pyle, 1990. Mauritius.

Only known from Mauritius, Réunion and the Aldabra Is. Prefers deep waters between 48–90 metres on steep outer reef drop-offs and vertical walls. Chest, snout and tail are bright yellow, and the rest is deeper blue overall. Also many black spots behind eye are characteristic. Reported to grow to 9 cm.

Remarks: named after the author HD, who discovered and collected this species in 1988. Recently recorded on Video in the Aldabra I., western Seychelles near Africa at a depth of only 20 m. Closely related to *C. nahackyi* and *C. multicolor*.

Aquarium: easily kept in captivity with or without inverts. Due to its rarity it is highly priced.

C. debelius. Réunion. Depth 60 m. Hugues Vitry.

C. debelius. Mauritius. Depth 52 m. Helmut Debelius.

C. debelius. Réunion. Depth 60 m. Hugues Vitry.

Cocos Pygmy Angelfish *Centropyge joculator*

Centropyge joculator Smith-Vaniz & Randall, 1974. Cocos-Keeling Island.

Restricted to Cocos-Keeling & Christmas Island, Indian Ocean. Lives on coral rubble and slopes in 8–70 m deep, usually in small groups. Readily identified by its bright yellow head with blue around the eye, with yellow extending onto body and ventral fins, and yellow tail. Attains 9 cm.

Remarks: appears to be closely related to *Centropyge debelius*, but looks somewhat similar to *C. hotumatua* from the south Pacific that is more orange.

Aquarium: can be kept safely with invertebrates and also does well in fish community tanks. On occasion shipped from Christmas Island where it is common, but usually highly priced.

A

C. joculator. Christmas I., Indian Ocean. L. 7 cm. Jerry Allen.

B

C

C. joculator. Christmas Island, Indian Ocean. Depth 17 m. Length 6 cm. Helmut Debelius.

D

C. joculator. Christmas Island, Indian Ocean. Depth 10 m. Length 8 cm. Roger Steene.

Hotumatua's Angelfish *Centropyge hotumatua*

Centropyge hotumatua Randall & Caldwell, 1973. Easter I.

Restricted to the Austral Is., Rapa, Pitcairn Group and Easter I. Inhabits crevices in rocky reefs or coral rubble areas at depths between 14–45 m. Fairly common below 25 m. Colour orange to yellow on head, face and chest and darker brown, dusky to black centrally. A blue and black half ring behind eye and a prominent black and blue spot just above and anterior to axil. Length to 9 cm. *Remarks*: first collected in 1969 and named for Hotumatua, a legendary Polynesian who first colonised Easter Island.

Aquarium: easily kept, but best in living reef type tank.

C. hotumatua. **A** aquarium. Large adult, length ~9 cm. Scott Michael. **B** aquarium. Subadult, length ~5 cm. Robert Myers.

Damsel Angelfish *Centropyge flavicauda*

Centropyge flavicauda Fraser-Brunner, 1933. South China Seas.

Widespread Indo-West Pacific, ranging from African coast, through South-east Asia, and in Pacific east to Tuamotu Archipelago. Juveniles range to subtropical zones. Occurs in small loose groups on coral rubble in gutters and also slopes at the bottom of drop-offs to at least 60 m depth. Easily overlooked as an angelfish as it occurs together with similar looking damselfishes in the same habitat. Length to 8 cm.

Remarks: closely related to *Centropyge fisheri* from Hawaii.

Aquarium: easy to keep in the home aquarium.

C. flavicauda. Bali, Indonesia. D. 15 m. L. 75 mm. Rudie Kuiter.

C. flavicauda. Aquarium, Australia. **B** from southern Qld. Length 40 mm. **C** juvenile from Sydney. Length 25 mm. Rudie Kuiter.

198

Fisher's Pygmy Angelfish *Centropyge fisheri*

Holacanthus fisheri Snyder, 1904. Hawaiian Islands.

Known only from the Hawaiian Islands and Midway Atoll. Found on coral rubble and lagoons at depths between 10–85 m. This species is brownish anteriorly and somewhat dusky on two thirds of body posteriorly. Some individuals are brown anteriorly and deeper blue posteriorly. Also it has a dark spot larger than the eye above pectoral fin base. Fins can be yellowish. A small species, length to 6cm.

Remarks: closely related to *C. flavicauda* that is dark bluish black overall with a whitish tail.

Aquarium: easy to keep and has been successfully bred in captivity.

A

C. fisheri. Adult. Aquarium. Length ~6 cm. Frank Schneidewind.

B

C. fisheri. Cultivated juvenile. Frank Baensch.

C

C. fisheri. Adult. Aquarium. Length ~5 cm. Frank Schneidewind.

D

C. fisheri. Adult. Hawaiian Islands. John Hoover.

African Pygmy Angelfish *Centropyge acanthops*
Holacanthus acanthops Norman, 1922. Durban, S. Africa.

Western Indian Ocean, east Africa from the Aliwal Shoal near Durban to Gulf of Aden, Oman, Madagascar, and to the Maldives. Prefers reef and rubble areas with good algae growth where in small loose groups on substrates to depths of at least 40 m, depending on the region. Mainly deep in the Aliwal Shoal and more shallow in coral regions. Lower fins and body mostly deep blue, bright yellow on head continuing over back and dorsal fin. Tail is also yellowish, and there is a thin blue ring around eye. Length to 8 cm.

Remarks: resembles Caribbean *Centropyge aurantonotus* but this has a blue tail.

Aquarium: very easy to keep in captivity and providing many smaller crevices helps them to settle in.

C. acanthops. Aquarium, from South Malé, Maldives. Rudie Kuiter.

C. acanthops. **B** aquarium. Length 8 cm. **C** Subadult. Kenya. Depth 15 m. Helmut Debelius.

C. acanthops. Shimoni reef, Kenya. Depth 15 m. Length 5 cm. Jerry Allen.

E

C. acanthops. Rocky habitat. Aliwal Shoal, South Africa. Depth 25 m. Length 5 cm. Rudie Kuiter.

F

C. acanthops. Coral habitat. Sodwana Bay, South Africa. Depth 15 m. Largest, probably male, about 7 cm. Rudie Kuiter.

Centropyge argi
Woods & Kanazawa, 1951.
Argus Bank, Bermuda I.

Western Atlantic Ocean, ranging from Bermuda, West Indies, Gulf of Mexico to south-eastern Brazil. A shallow water species that can be seen in 5–10 metres depth, but often in deeper waters below 30 metres in coral reefs and on rubble bottoms. Almost deep blue with yellow around face and chest. Bright blue rims on each fin. Length to 65 mm.

Remarks: its close relatives *Centropyge aurantonotus* and *C. resplendens* are easily distinguished by colour.

Aquarium: this pygmy angelfish is one of the easiest to keep and has been known for a long time. Several individuals can be kept and spawning happens often.

C. argi. Caribbean. L. 6 cm. D. 10 m. Robert Meyers.

C. argi. Bonaire, Caribbean. L. 4 cm. D. 10 m. Roger Steene.

C. argi. Aquarium. Length 55 mm. Rudie Kuiter.

C. argi. Aquarium. **D** length 5 cm. Helmut Debelius. **E** length 6 cm. Frank Schneidewind.

Flameback Pygmy Angelfish *Centropyge aurantonotus*

Centropyge aurantonotus Burgess, 1974.
Barbados, West Indies.

Southern Caribbean Sea, Lesser Anthilles, Curacao, Barbados, St. Lucia and south to Brazil. Mostly found on open substrates with remote patches of staghorn corals and rubble areas in depths between 16 to 200 m. Usually seen shallower at depths of 16–25 m. Body and lower fins metallic blue and caudal fin dark, abruptly changing to orange-yellow above the lateral line and head. When young dark blue area covers most of the body. Length to 6 cm.

Remarks: one of a complex of 3 blue-and-yellow species, comprising *Centropyge argi* (Caribbean to Brazil), and *C. resplendens* (Ascension, mid Atlantic Ocean). However, not including the superficially similar *C. acanthops* from the Indian Ocean, that is more closely related to *C. fisheri* and *C. flavicauda*.

Aquarium: a somewhat rare species in the aquarium trade.

C. aurantonotus. Adult, aquarium. Frank Schneidewind.	*C. aurantonotus*. Arraial do Cabo, Brazil. Carlos Ferreira.

Resplendent Pygmy Angelfish *Centropyge resplendens*

Centropyge resplendens Lubbock & Sankey, 1975. Ascension Island.

Known only from Ascension Island, mid Atlantic Ocean. Occurs on rubble and rocky seabeds at depths between 15–40 m. Back, nose, dorsal and caudal fins bright orange-yellow and the rest brilliant blue. A posterior part of anal fin usually has more yellow in male individuals. Length to 6 cm, but most specimens to 4–5 cm.

Remarks: closely related to *Centropyge argi* and *C. aurantonotus*

from the Caribbean. These species are easily distinguished from each other by comparing colour patterns.

Aquarium: on occasion this species will appear in the aquarium trade, especially in the UK, but it always demands a high price. Keeping them in reef tanks is most desirable, and several specimens can be kept in the same tank. They may spawn in home aquaria and reproduce if well cared for.

C. resplendes. Ascension Island. Roger Lubbock.	*C. resplendes*. Ascension Island. Marcel Staebler.

Deep-reef Pygmy Angelfish
Centropyge narcosis

Centropyge narcosis Pyle & Randall, 1992.
Cook Islands.

Endemic to the Cook Islands, south Pacific. This species occurs in depths greater than 100 m. Seen in caves or crevices of walls on outer drop-offs. Observed singly or in a small group. A very distinctive species, being bright yellow all over with just a prominent black spot on its side, and a tall dorsal fin. Length to about 8 cm.

Remarks: was first discovered in 1989 and, due to its great depth preference, is one of the most out of reach species in the wild.

Aquarium: apparently fairly easy to keep in captivity, but should be kept together with a few other, carefully selected fishes, as well as providing a dim environment in the aquarium and surroundings.

C. narcosis. Aquarium. Holotype. Cook Islands. Richard Pyle.

Black-spot Pygmy Angelfish
Centropyge nigriocellus

Centropyge nigriocellus Woods & Schultz, 1953.
Johnston I., Pacific.

Central Pacific, Tinian, the Marianas, Admiralty, Samoan, Society, Line and Johnston Islands. Occurs on coral rubble in lagoons and outer reefs at depths between 4–15 m. A highly secretive species that is easily overlooked by divers, and there are no reports of observations in the wild. Has a pale yellow body with two prominent black spots, one on pectoral fin base and one posteriorly on soft dorsal fin. Caudal fin whitish and other fins pale. Length to 6 cm.

Aquarium: successfully kept in the Steinhart Aquarium.

C. nigriocellus. Aquarium. Specimen from Johnston Island. Richard Pyle.

Colin's Pygmy Angelfish *Centropyge colini*

Centropyge colini Smith-Vaniz & Randall, 1974.
Cocos-Keeling Islands.

Scattered Pacific and eastern Indian Ocean localities, Indonesia, Papua New Guinea, Solomons, Fiji, Palau, Guam, the Philippines, north to Ogasawara Islands and Cocos-Keeling, south of Java. A very shy and rarely seen species usually found upside down in caves, or under steep walls where it is darker, at depths of 24 to over 75 m. It is mostly yellow with a large blue area on back and spinous part of dorsal fin. Length to 9 cm.

Remarks: it has a fairly deep body and it does not appear to have close relatives.

Aquarium: rather difficult to maintain in captivity over a long period.

A

C. colini. Aquarium. From Indonesia. L. 5 cm. Fenton Walsh.

B

C

C. colini. Milne Bay, Papua New Guinea. Depth 55 m. Bob Halstead.

D

E

C. colini. **D** Milne Bay, Papua New Guinea. D. 55 m. Bob Halstead. **E** Guam. Length 7 cm. Robert Myers.

BIBLIOGRAPHY

Allen, Gerald R, 1980. *Butterfly and Angelfishes of the World.* John Wiley & Sons, New York.

Allen, Gerald R., Ross Robertson, 1994. *Fishes of the Tropical Eastern Pacific.* Crawford House Press, Bathurst, New South Wales.

Allen, Gerald R., Roger Steene & Mark Allen, 1998. *A Guide to Angelfishes & Butterflyfishes.* Odyssey, USA/Tropical Reef Research, Aust.

Debelius, Helmut, 1997. *Mediterranean and Atlantic Fish Guide.* IKAN-Unterwasserarchiv, Germany.

Debelius, Helmut, 1998. *Red Sea Reef Guide.* IKAN-Unterwasserarchiv, Germany.

Edwards, Alasdair, 1990. Fish and Fisheries of Saint Helena Island. Gov. St. Helena.

Gloerfelt-Tarp, Thomas & Patricia J. Kailola. *Trawled Fishes of Southern Indonesia and Northwestern Australia.*

Humann, Paul, 1997. *Fisch Führer Karibik.* Jhar Verlag Hamburg.

King, Dennis, 1997. *Reef Fishes & Corals.* Struik Publishers P/L. Cape Town.

King, Dennis, & Valda Fraser 2002. *More Reef Fishes & Nudibranchs.* Struik Publishers P/L. Cape Town.

Kuiter, Rudie H., 1992. *Tropical Reef-Fishes of the Western Pacific Indonesia and Adjacent Waters.* Penerbit PT Gramedia Pustaka Utama, Jakarta.

Kuiter, Rudie H., 1996. *Guide to Sea Fishes of Australia.* New Holland Publishers, Australia.

Kuiter, Rudie H., 1998. *Photo Guide to Fishes of the Maldives.* Atoll Editions. Apollo Bay.

Kuiter, Rudie H., 2000. *Coastal Fishes of South-Eastern Australia.* Gary Allen ty Ltd. Sydney, Australia.

Kuiter, Rudie H., & Helmut Debelius. 1994. *Southeast Asia Tropical Fish Guide.* IKAN-Unterwasserarchiv, Germany.

Kuiter, Rudie H., & Takamasa Tonozuka 2001. *Indonesian Reef Fishes.* Zoonetics. Seaford, Australia. 3 volumes.

Masuda, Hajime, et al, 1984. *The Fishes of the Japanese Archipelago.* Tokai University Press. Tokyo.

Merlen, Godfrey, 1988. *A Field Guide to the Fishes of Galápagos.* Wilmot Books, London.

Myers, Robert F., 1999. *Micronesian Reef Fishes.* Coral Graphics. Guam.

Nakabo, Tetsuji, 1993. *Fishes of Japan with Pictorial keys to The Species.* Tokai University Press. Tokyo.

Nakabo, Tetsuji, 2002. *Fishes of Japan with Pictorial keys to The Species, English edition.* Tokai Un. Press. Tokyo.

Schneidewind, Frank, 1999. *Kaiserfische.* Tetra-Verlag, Bissendork-Wulften.

Smith, Margaret M. & Phillip C. Heemstra, 1986. *Smith's Seafishes.* Springer-Verlag.

Steene, Roger C., 1978. *Butterfly and Angelfishes of the World.* A.H. & A.W. Reed P/L, Wellington.

INDEX TO SCIENTIFIC AND COMMON NAMES

acanthops, **Centropyge** **200**
African Pygmy Angelfish **200**
africanus, **Holacanthus** **66**
Angelfish **20**
  African Pygmy **200**
  Ballina **122**
  Bandit **98**
  Black **128**
  Black Tiger **181**
  Black Velvet **112**
  Black-spot **143**
  Black-spot Pygmy **204**
  Blue **74**
  Blue & Gold **176**
  Blue Mauritius **196**
  Blue Vermiculate **110**
  Blue-back **162**
  Blue-face **26**
  Blue-girdled **20**
  Blue-ringed **30**

Angelfish
  Blue-striped **102**
  Candy-striped **167**
  Clarion **80**
  Clipperton **82**
  Cocos Pygmy **197**
  Colin's Pygmy **205**
  Cortez **50**
  Crescent **40**
  Damsel **198**
  Deep-reef Pygmy **204**
  Ear-spot **33**
  Eibl's **182**
  Fisher's Pygmy **199**
  Flame **188**
  Flameback Pygmy **203**
  French **56**
  Golden **185**
  Golden-spotted **94**
  Grey **54**

Angelfish
  Grey-tail **132**
  Griffis **96**
  Half-banded **150**
  Herald's **174**
  Hotumatua's **198**
  Japanese **148**
  Japanese Pygmy **192**
  Keyhole **172**
  King **78**
  Lamarck's **140**
  Lemonpeel **178**
  Many-banded **164**
  Many-colour Pygmy **194**
  Many-spined **183**
  Masked **158**
  Maze **106**
  Midnight **173**
  Nahacky's Pygmy **195**
  Old Woman **38**

Angelfish
Ornate 142
Pale-head Velvet 114
Pearly-scaled 180
Personifer 121
Phanthom 116
Pitcairn 152
Potter's 191
Queen 68
Regal 134
Resplendent Pygmy 203
Réunion 96
Rusty 190
Scribbled 124
Semicircle 46
Shepard's 189
Six-banded 23
Smoke 87
Spectacled 126
Takeuchi's 155
Three-spot 88
Tiger 92
Velvet 112
Vermiculate 130
Watanabe's 153
West African 66
Woodhead's 175
Yellow-blotch 42
Yellow-tail 118
Queensland 118
Yellowfin 184
Zebra 146
Angelichthys 64
annularis, Pomacanthus 30
Apolemichthys 84
   arcuatus 98
   Xarmitagei 91
   griffisi 96
   guezei 96
   kingi 92
   kingi X trimaculatus 91
   trimaculatus 88
   xanthopunctatus 94
   xanthotis 87
   xanthurus 86
Arabian Smoke-angelfish 87
arcuatus, Apolemichthys 98
arcuatus, Pomacanthus 54
argi, Centropyge 202
asfur, Pomacanthus 40
aurantia, Centropyge 185
aurantonotus, Centropyge 203
Ballina Angelfish 122
ballinae, Chaetodontoplus 122
Bandit Angelfish 98
bellus, Genicanthus 142
bermudensis, Holacanthus 74
bicolor, Centropyge 176
bispinosa, Centropyge 186

Black Angelfish 128
Black Tiger Angelfish 181
Black Velvet Angelfish 112
Black-spot Angelfish 143
Black-spot Pygmy Angelfish 204
Blue & Gold Angelfish 176
Blue Angelfish 74
Blue Mauritius Angelfish 196
Blue Vermiculate Angelfish 110
Blue-back Angelfish 162
Blue-face Angelfish 26
Blue-girdled Angelfish 20
Blue-ringed angelfish 30
Blue-striped Angelfish 102
boylei, Paracentropyge 167
caeruleopunctatus, Chaetodontoplus 110
Candy-striped Angelfish 167
caudovittatus, Genicanthus ...146
Centropyge 168
   acanthops 200
   argi 202
   aurantia 185
   aurantonotus 203
   bicolor 176
   bispinosa 186
   colini 205
   debelius 196
   eibli 182
   ferrugata 190
   fisheri 199
   flavicauda 198
   flavipectoralis 184
   flavissima 178
   heraldi 174
   hotumatua 198
   interrupta 192
   joculator 197
   loriculus 188
   multicolor 194
   multispinis 183
   nahackyi 195
   narcosis 204
   nigriocellus 204
   nox 173
   potteri 191
   resplendens 203
   shepardi 189
   tibicen 172
   vrolikii 180
   vrolikii, cf 181
   woodheadi 175
cephalareticulatus, Chaetodontoplus 106
Chaetodontoplus 100
   ballinae 122
   caeruleopunctatus 110
   cephalareticulatus 106
   chrysocephalus 110
   conspicillatus 126
   dimidiatus 116

Chaetodontoplus
   duboulayi 124
   melanosoma 112
   melanosoma, cf 114
   meredithi 118
   mesoleucus 130
   mesoleucus, cf 132
   niger 128
   personifer 121
   septentrionalis 102
Cherubfish 202
chrysocephalus, Chaetodontoplus ..110
chrysurus, Pomacanthus 33
ciliaris, Holacanthus 68
Clarion Angelfish 80
clarionensis, Holacanthus 80
Clipperton Angelfish 82
Cocos Pygmy Angelfish 197
Colin's Pygmy Angelfish 205
colini, Centropyge 205
conspicillatus, Chaetodontoplus ..126
Coral Beauty 186
Cortez Angelfish 50
Crescent Angelfish 40
Damsel Angelfish 198
debelius, Centropyge 196
Deep-reef Pygmy Angelfish 204
diacanthus, Pygoplites 134
dimidiatus, Chaetodontoplus ...116
duboulayi, Chaetodontoplus ...124
Ear-spot Angelfish 33
Eibl's Angelfish 182
eibli, Centropyge 182
Emperor Angelfish 34
ferrugata, Centropyge 190
Fisher's Pygmy Angelfish 199
fisheri, Centropyge 199
Flame Angelfish 188
Flameback Pygmy Angelfish 203
flavicauda, Centropyge 198
flavipectoralis, Centropyge ...184
flavissima, Centropyge 178
French Angelfish 56
Genicanthus 138
   bellus 142
   caudovittatus 146
   lamarck 140
   melanospilos 143
   personatus 158
   semicinctus 150
   semifasciatus 148
   spinus 152
   takeuchii 155
   watanabei 153
Golden Angelfish 185
Golden-spotted Angelfish 94
Grey Angelfish 54
Grey-tail Angelfish 132
Griffis' Angelfish 96

griffisi, *Apolemichthys* 96
guezei, *Apolemichthys* 96
Half-banded Angelfish 150
Herald's Angelfish 174
heraldi, *Centropyge* 174
Holacanthus 60
    africanus 66
    bermudensis 74
    ciliaris .68
    clarionensis 80
    limbaughi 82
    passer 78
    tricolor 61
Hotumatua's Angelfish 198
hotumatua, *Centropyge* 198
imperator, *Pomacanthus* 34
Indian Smoke-angelfish 86
interrupta, *Centropyge* 192
Japanese Pygmy Angelfish 192
Japanese Swallow 148
joculator, *Centropyge* 197
Keyhole Angelfish 172
King Angelfish 78
kingi, *Apolemichthys* 92
Lamarck's Angelfish 140
lamarck, *Genicanthus* 140
Lemonpeel Angelfish 178
limbaughi, *Holacanthus* 82
loriculus, *Centropyge* 188
maculosus, *Pomacanthus* 42
Many-banded Angelfish 164
Many-colour Pygmy Angelfish 194
Many-spined Angelfish 183
Masked Angelfish 158
Maze Angelfish 106
melanosoma, *Chaetodontoplus* 112
melanospilos, *Genicanthus* 143
meredithi, *Chaetodontoplus* 118
mesoleucus, *Chaetodontoplus* 130
Midnight Angelfish 173
multicolor, *Centropyge* 194
multifasciata, *Paracentropyge* 164
multispinis, *Centropyge* 183
Nahacky's Pygmy Angelfish 195
nahackyi, *Centropyge* 195
narcosis, *Centropyge* 204
navarchus, *Pomacanthus* 20
niger, *Chaetodontoplus* 128
nigriocellus, *Centropyge* 204
nox, *Centropyge* 173
Old Woman Angelfish 38

Ornate Angelfish 142
Pale-head Velvet Angelfish 114
Paracentropyge 160
    boylei 167
    multifasciata 164
    venusta 162
paru, *Pomacanthus* 56
passer, *Holacanthus* 78
Pearly-scaled Angelfish 180
personatus, *Genicanthus* 158
Personifer Angelfish 121
personifer, *Chaetodontoplus* 121
Phanthom Angelfish 116
Pitcairn Angelfish 152
Plitops 76
Pomacanthodes 29
Pomacanthus 20
    annularis 30
    arcuatus 54
    asfur 40
    chrysurus 33
    imperator 34
    maculosus 42
    navarchus 20
    paru 56
    rhomboides 38
    semicirculatus 46
    sexstriatus 23
    xanthometopon 26
    zonipectus 50
Potter's Angelfish 191
potteri, *Centropyge* 191
Pygmy Angelfish 192
    African 200
    Black-spot 204
    Cocos 197
    Colin's 205
    Deep-reef 204
    Fisher's 199
    Flameback 203
    Japanese 192
    Nahacky's 195
    Resplendent 203
Pygoplites 134
    diacanthus 134
Queen Angelfish 68
Queensland Yellow-tail Angelfish . . .118

Regal Angelfish 134
resplendens, *Centropyge* 203
Resplendent Pygmy Angelfish 203
Réunion Angelfish 96
rhomboides, *Pomacanthus* 38
Rock Beauty 61
Rusty Angelfish 190
Scribbled Angelfish 124
semicinctus, *Genicanthus* 150
Semicircle Angelfish 46
semicirculatus, *Pomacanthus* 46
semifasciatus, *Genicanthus* 148
septentrionalis, *Chaetodontoplus* . . .102
sexstriatus, *Pomacanthus* 23
Shepard's Angelfish 189
shepardi, *Centropyge* 189
Six-banded Angelfish 23
Smoke-angelfish 87
    Arabian 87
    Hybrid 91
    Indian 86
Spectacled Angelfish 126
spinus, *Genicanthus* 152
Takeuchi's Angelfish 155
takeuchii, *Genicanthus* 155
Three-spot Angelfish 88
tibicen, *Centropyge* 172
Tiger Angelfish 92
tricolor, *Holacanthus* 61
trimaculatus, *Apolemichthys* 88
Velvet Angelfish 112
    Black .112
    Pale-head 114
venusta, *Paracentropyge* 162
Vermiculate Angelfish 130
vrolikii, *Centropyge* 180
Watanabe's Angelfish 153
watanabei, *Genicanthus* 153
West African Angelfish 66
Woodhead's Angelfish 175
woodheadi, *Centropyge* 175
xanthometopon, *Pomacanthus* 26
xanthopunctatus, *Apolemichthys* . . .94
xanthotis, *Apolemichthys* 87
xanthurus, *Apolemichthys* 86
Yellow-blotch Angelfish 42
Yellow-tail Angelfish 118
    Queensland 118
Yellowfin Angelfish 184
Zebra Angelfish 146
zonipectus, *Pomacanthus* 50